BERGEN-BELSEN 1945

A Medical Student's Journal

BERGEN-BELSEN 1945

A Medical Student's Journal

by

Michael John Hargrave

Imperial College Press

Published by

Imperial College Press
57 Shelton Street
Covent Garden
London WC2H 9HE

Distributed by

World Scientific Publishing Co. Pte. Ltd.
5 Toh Tuck Link, Singapore 596224
USA office: 27 Warren Street, Suite 401-402, Hackensack, NJ 07601
UK office: 57 Shelton Street, Covent Garden, London WC2H 9HE

British Library Cataloguing-in-Publication Data
A catalogue record for this book is available from the British Library.

Front cover: A general view of the Bergen-Belsen concentration camp from outside the perimenter fence, April 1945. © Imperial War Museum (BU 2768).

ISBN 978-1-78326-320-2
ISBN 978-1-78326-288-5 (pbk)

Typeset by Stallion Press
Email: enquiries@stallionpress.com

Printed by FuIsland Offset Printing (S) Pte Ltd Singapore

Dedicated to all who suffered in the Holocaust

Foreword

In early May 1945, six Dakotas set off from an airfield near Cirencester and crossed the Channel, heading for Celle in Germany. Their cargo was 95 medical students, recruited hastily from six London medical schools — among them 21-year-old Michael Hargrave, midway through his studies at the Westminster Hospital. The initial purpose of the exercise had been to assist starving civilians in Holland, but there was a change of plan and the students were sent instead as emergency back-up to assist in the care of survivors at the recently liberated Bergen-Belsen concentration camp. The wartime experiences of these young men had been confined to the Home Front — completing their matriculation and Higher School Certificates and then starting their training at medical school. The four weeks they spent at the camp tested both their medical skills and their personal stamina to an unimaginable degree.

The camp at Bergen-Belsen presented a humanitarian disaster of colossal proportions. Its history within the Nazi camp system was somewhat unusual — it had been a so-called 'exchange camp' where inmates were held with a view to possible exchange for German prisoners of war. But, by April 1945, its population had risen considerably as the Nazis moved thousands of camp survivors out of camps in Poland and sent them west — either by cattle truck or on foot. The camp commandant, Josef Kramer, notoriously failed to provide for the needs of his suddenly hopelessly overcrowded camp and the German Army surrendered the camp to the British under a special truce, some three weeks ahead of the actual German capitulation.

When the British arrived on 15 April, the first and most urgent task was to bury the bodies of some 10,000 camp inmates who had died. The Army medical authorities were then faced with the massive task of saving those they could whilst at the same time preventing the spread of disease. An evacuation plan was drawn up which would eventually see the inmates of Camp 1 cleaned, disinfected and transferred from the camp. But, before this could happen, each hut had to be cleared and disinfected and became a temporary hospital — albeit in very primitive conditions.

Bespectacled and, in a team photograph, looking as though he is scarcely out of school, Hargrave was put in charge of Hut 210. In his diary, Hargrave provides a detailed account of how this place was gradually transformed into a temporary hospital, pending the full evacuation of Camp 1. The students turned their hands to all kinds of tasks, from hosing down the huts with creosol to making straw-filled mattresses. Systems were established and nursing accommodation of sorts was sectioned off within the hut. Hargrave is punctilious in describing the various ailments he treated, providing drawings of particular surgical cases, such as a cyst on an eyelid or tuberculous glands in the neck. The medical students soon became experts in the particular diseases of the camp — diarrhoea, typhus and severe malnutrition, as well as terrible sores, boils and gangrenous conditions — and were able to make crucial interventions, for example persuading the Army Blood Transfusion Service to stop giving transfusions to patients with severe oedema. (Typhus weakened the heart and the patients could not take the treatment.) Hargrave muses over the causes of the diarrhoea — was it mechanical or infective? And what were the implications for further liberations of camps in the Far East? We have the impression of a youthful, enquiring man, slightly frustrated at times to be missing the Victory celebrations in Britain, but totally focussed on the needs of his patients.

We also get occasional glimpses of some of the wider protagonists in this story: Dr Meiklejohn, the nutrition expert, gives them a talk about the challenges the medical services face on their arrival and there are subsequent briefings from Colonel Johnston, the Senior Medical Officer in charge of the camp, and from Brigadier Glyn-Hughes, Deputy Director of Medical Services.

The reader is aware that the conditions were appalling, but Hargrave concentrates mainly on the medical detail and on the vital organisational challenges which ultimately saved many hundreds of lives. Diagrams provide a useful record of the layout of various huts and facilities including the Human Laundry, where, at 17 separate tables, four-strong teams of German nurses worked simultaneously on one patient, washing them and powdering them with the now banned pesticide DDT. Not everyone had the necessary training for the task and at one point Hargrave admonishes himself for not being there when an untrained nurse made a fatal mistake. Again, Hargrave does not labour the point, and we also learn that several of the medics contracted the diseases they were trying to treat — 'several chaps down with diarrhoea and vomiting'.

As Hargrave got to know some of his patients, the word 'Auschwitz' appears in several reported conversations. But the full facts of what we now call the Holocaust had yet to be fully understood. He teaches a young Polish survivor — Zosia Wisniowksa — to speak English — a useful move as ward rounds are made much more effective when language barriers are overcome. Hargrave seems a little smitten by Zosia and she gives him her address in Krakow, although whether they remained in touch is not known.

Hargrave's account is one of several held by the Documents and Sound Section at the Imperial War Museum (IWM). After the Bergen-Belsen Information Centre itself, ours is the richest collection of material on the liberation and relief operation at the camp, with no fewer than nine collections of private papers deposited by former medical student volunteers. With the increased interest in IWM as a resource for medical history, these diaries and letters have been used a great deal by scholars and more 'popular' writers alike, keen to better understand how the British military authorities dealt with this major human catastrophe. Michael Hargrave's account was one of the very first of the medical students' records to be deposited in the IWM's archive, being presented in 1968 prior to his untimely death at the age of 50. As a result, his diary has been particularly widely used, perhaps most notably by the historian Ben Shephard, whose book *After Daybreak: The Liberation of Belsen 1945* (Pimlico, London, 2006) remains the most detailed recent work on the relief of the camp. To have Michael Hargrave's informative and vivid account published is an invaluable addition to the literature on this subject.

Suzanne Bardgett
Head of Research
Imperial War Museum
London, June 2013

Amnesty International UK

When the young Michael Hargrave arrived in Belsen he found himself faced with unspeakable horrors. He and his fellow students provided basic medical care as the world was only just beginning to comprehend the crimes inflicted in Nazi concentration camps. As international outrage grew, so too did momentum for a global human rights agenda to say 'never again'. In 1948 the Universal Declaration of Human Rights (UDHR) was adopted. It was the first document to agree common, global terms for what we know to be right and just.

Amnesty International is rooted in the UDHR. We believe in the power of ordinary people to make extraordinary change, just as Michael Hargrave and his comrades did at Bergen-Belsen. And we find, over and again, that the act of bearing witness to atrocities and injustice is invaluable on the path to understanding and changing for the better. Michael bore meticulous witness in his journal and, even in publication nearly 70 years later, it still has much to teach us today.

Amnesty International's vision is of a world where everyone enjoys all our human rights. In pursuit of this we undertake research and action focussed on preventing and ending grave abuses. You can find out more and take action yourself at www.amnesty.org.uk.

The Human Rights Action Centre
17–25 New Inn Yard
London EC2A 3EA
020 7033 1500
sct@amnesty.org.uk
www.amnesty.org.uk

Rotary and Polio

Rotary began its PolioPlus campaign to immunise the children of the world against polio in 1985, following an extremely successful immunisation campaign in the Philippines.

In 1988 Rotarians were joined in their fight by WHO, UNICEF and CDC, and, in 2009, The Bill & Melinda Gates Foundation.

It is estimated that there were at least 1,000 cases of paralytic polio occurring *every day* at the start of the campaign, but records were incomplete in those days. By 2010 that figure had dropped to 1,000 in the *whole year*, and in 2012 there were just 223 infected children — although still 223 too many.

At the start of the campaign, polio was endemic in most countries in the world. That figure now stands at just three — Afghanistan, Nigeria and Pakistan.

Over US$12 billion has been spent so far, and over 2 billion children have been immunised at a cost of US$0.60 each.

However, as long as there remains one unimmunised child, the risk of polio recurring still exists.

The aim of Rotary International and its partners is to eradicate the virus from the face of the earth. Don't forget, polio is just a plane ride away.

PolioPlus
c/o Rotary Foundation UK
Kinwarton Road
Alcester
Warwickshire B49 6BP
01789 765411
RFUK@ribi.org

Dr Michael John Hargrave LRCP. MRCS. MRCGP.

8 December 1923–25 July 1974

Michael Hargrave was born in Simla, India, where his father, a decorated First World War pilot, was posted while serving in the Royal Air Force. He was the eldest of two boys and was educated at Harcourt Preparatory School at Weyhill, and then attended St Edward's School, Oxford. In 1942, after leaving school, he went to King's College London University and then to Westminster Hospital to undertake his clinical training to become a doctor.

In April 1945, Michael, 21 years old and in his fourth year of medical school, responded to a notice: 'please sign below'. At first, he and the 95 volunteers were not told what they were signing up for, but they were later informed they were being sent to Holland to assist starving civilians. On the day of departure, however, the medical students learnt that their destination had been changed: they were now bound for the recently liberated Bergen-Belsen concentration camp in north-western Germany.

With no doctors available, the camp was in dire need of medical assistance and, to this end, the medical students had been drafted in to help. During his month-long experience at the camp, Michael kept a journal for his mother, and it is this which is published in its entirety here. It gives a clear insight into the horrendous conditions under which the prisoners were living and the tireless attempts made by the British troops and medical students to try and help these unfortunate people. The diary provides many detailed descriptions of diseases encountered within the camp, and these are interspersed amongst more 'light-hearted' entries recounting the minutiae of day-to-day life.

Upon returning from Bergen-Belsen, Michael qualified as a doctor in January 1947 and worked for a year as a houseman at Westminster Hospital. In 1948, he married a nurse from the hospital, Joy Thompson, and, after two years of National Service in the RAF in Kenya, he returned to the UK to become a general practitioner (GP) in Wootton Bassett. He worked there for 24 years but sadly, in 1974, he was diagnosed with a brain tumour and died at the age of 50. He is survived by his wife and two children. In 1953, both his children developed polio. David, his son, recovered fully, but his daughter Sally, aged nine months, was admitted to an isolation hospital for two months and then spent a further three months in hospital; she was left with a paralysed right leg. She had several operations over the next few years and the first birthday she was able to celebrate at home was her fourth birthday. In adult life she became a successful shorthand typist, while David followed in his father's footsteps and became a GP in Portland, Dorset.

Diseases at Bergen-Belsen

Epidemic Typhus

Typhus is a disease caused by the *Rickettsia prowazeki* bacteria. It occurs in over-crowded and unhygienic conditions as found in army camps or jails. As such, it is often called 'jail fever'. An infected person is bitten by a louse which sucks his blood and the louse becomes infected in turn. When a louse bites it defecates at the same time and the bacteria is excreted in its faeces. It is the scratching of the area of the bite that allows bacteria to penetrate the skin and be rubbed into open wounds, causing the infection to spread to another person.

Following an incubation period of 7–14 days, the onset of illness is abrupt with symptoms of prostration, severe headache, high fever, cough, photophobia, red-ness of the conjunctiva and severe muscular pain. A rash appears on the fifth day, mainly on the trunk. Confusion and coma are common. Untreated disease can prove to be fatal in up to 40% of cases. Today, treatment is administered in the form of doxycycline tablets.

At Bergen-Belsen there was a severe outbreak of typhus in February and March 1945 and it is estimated that 20,000–30,000 people died from typhus, typhoid, tuberculosis and dysentery.

Typhoid or Enteric Fever

Typhoid is caused by bacteria *Salmonella* Typhi and *Salmonella* Paratyphi. It is transmitted through the ingestion of contaminated food or water or from close contact with infected people. The incubation period is about two weeks. There is usually a gradual onset of headache, aching in the limbs, tiredness, cough and fever which typically intensify incrementally. At the end of the first week small pink spots appear on the abdomen and chest known as 'rose spots'. Most people suffer from constipation for the first few days but in the second week the abdomen becomes distended and diarrhoea sets in — 'pea soup stools' up to 20 times a day. Patients become gravely ill and may lapse into a coma. Most patients improve over three to four weeks but there is a mortality rate of about 15% in untreated patients. Approximately 1–5% of patients become long-term carriers. Today, the best way to avoid contracting typhoid is maintaining good food and water hygiene, as well as being vaccinated against typhoid. The current treatment for the disease is with antibiotics.

Acknowledgements

I would like to take this opportunity to thank Mr Phillip Barlow, Senior Library Assistant at the Chelsea and Westminster Hospital, who earlier this year read my father's journal and encouraged me to consider having it published. I would also like to thank him for producing the valuable and informative glossary.

I am most grateful to Suzanne Bardgett, Head of Research at the Imperial War Museum, for writing a most interesting and detailed foreword to this journal.

I would like to thank Getty Images, the Imperial War Museum and the Press Association for granting licences for me to publish their images which I have used in this book. I am also extremely grateful to the Evening News/Associated Newspapers and Evening Standard/Independent for granting permission free of charge to publish the newspaper cuttings which my father collected along the way. Thank you.

A very big thank you must go to Imperial College Press for agreeing to publish this journal. The staff have been extremely supportive in guiding me through the process and special thanks must go to Alice Oven, Tasha D'Cruz, Roberta Cucuzza, Dominic Graham and Tom Stottor for all their work in helping to collate the book.

Poliomyelitis was one of the most feared childhood illnesses of the twentieth century. It was not until 1955, when the first injectable Salk vaccine was introduced in the UK, and 1957, when the oral Sabin vaccine drops given on sugar lumps became available, that the disease was finally conquered. The Rotary Club PolioPlus campaign in conjunction with The Bill & Melinda Gates Foundation has virtually eradicated this disease around the world. It is their vision that polio will be entirely eradicated in the near future. Unfortunately, the vaccinations came a year or two too late for my family as my sister and I were affected by polio in 1953. If my father were still alive now I know he would have supported this cause. I would like to thank Dr Keith Barnard Jones, the UK lead in the PolioPlus campaign, for his enthusiastic support in the promotion of this publication.

The appalling abuse of human rights in Belsen during the Second World War shocked the entire world and it is my belief that the protection and defence of human rights is of great importance to prevent such colossal abuse from recurring. For this reason I have always been an admirer of the work of Amnesty International and I would like to thank Nicky Parker and Maggie Paterson from Amnesty International UK for their help and support in promoting the book.

For the above reasons I am pleased to donate all royalties from this book to be shared equally between Amnesty International and the Rotary Club PolioPlus campaign.

My final thanks must go to my mother for giving permission to allow my father's journal to be published. I hope she will be pleased with the completed book.

Dr David B. Hargrave

BELSEN-BERGEN. DIARY.

MAY 1945.

M.J. Hargrave,
Westminster Hospital,
London.

SATURDAY April 28th.

Got up in battledress to-day and went to the Hospital. Met all the others there - and as there was no new notice up did not expect to leave. However George Woodwark phoned up the Red Cross at Lowndes Street and they said that we were to meet at 5, Lowndes Street at 2 o'clock in the afternoon.

Just beforellunch we were told that we were going to be photographed for a Press Agency so we had to get into all our equipment and then followed some very faked photographs of me shaking hands with the Dean - supposed to be saying good-bye.

After lunch we piled into taxis with all our equipment and drove off to Lowndes Street - still rather doubtful if it was really true that we were off at last. These doubts were soon dispelled when we arrived and found about 80 other students from the other Hospitals waiting on the pavement.

After waiting for about half an hour we went upstairs and collected our passports, military permits and cards bearing our rank if we were captured.

We were then told that we were not going to Holland at all - but that we were going to Belsen Concentration Camp, that the Camp had been liberated for 10 days and that all they had succeeded in doing was to separate the living from the dead; - this was the first news we had been given about going to Belsen but we were all so excited about going, after a month of waiting, that we did not think much about the change of destination.

We were told that we would be going up to Cirencester by the
6.30 train and that we would be flying over the next morning; so
we hung around sitting on the steps of the nearby houses until about
4.30 when nine army lorries drove up to take us to Paddington.

Drove through London - after more Press photographs had been
taken - singing Clementine etc. and eventually arrived at Paddington,
where it began to rain, got on to the platform and were told that we
could wander off and get some tea.

Derek Wells and I joined a long queue and eventually got some
tea which was not worth drinking, and then went back to the platform
to find that Lionel Garstin had got hold of a late edition of the
Evening News, with a photograph/of us taken that morning outside
in it
Westminster.

Got on the train and we all settled down to read, the journey
passed quite quickly and the weather got progressively worse, until
when we arrived at Cirencester it was raining, dark, and very cold,
- all our baggage got mixed up, blankets got extremely wet - but
eventually we all managed to get aboard the lorries which were going
to take us to the Transit Camp.

We arrived at the Transit Camp after about a 20 minute drive
and as we got out of the lorries it began to snow!

Eventually after what appeared to be endless walking, all of
us from Westminster found ourselves occupying a Nissen Hut No.5.,
which contained 12 wooden beds with palliases and a stove which was
completely empty and on looking round we found that one of the
windows was broken so we had an icy wind blowing into the hut.

Went down to the Cookhouse, which was about 400 yards away but seemed much further, to have a meal which was very welcome - the time was about 10.30, we were told that the N.A.A.F.I. would open at 11o'clock till 11.30 for us and that we were free to use the Officers Mess.

We were also told that we would have to get up at 4.30 the next morning with breakfast at 5.0 o'clock.

We went to bed dressed in long pants, sweaters, socks, and with everything over us which we could lay hands on, and settled down to a cold and miserable night.

SUNDAY April 29th.

We had a very cold and miserable night - we were woken up at 4.30 by one of the cooks and dressed as quickly as we could in order to keep warm. We went out to have a wash and found that the wash house consisted of a wooden board set with taps, in a small corrugated iron shed which had no door and windows with no glass in them. After a very skimpy wash, had breakfast. Came back to the hut, packed up, this time wrapping my blankets up in my waterproof cape, and staggered out to where the lorries were waiting to take us to the Airport.

We all piled on board and left the Transit Camp, forever as we hoped, had about a 55 minute journey and then arrived at Down Aphny Aerodrome, drove onto the Airstrip and dismounted, we were then split up into parties of 16, according to alphabetical order, this made six

parties - I was in No.2.   After about half an hour we got onto our
lorries in parties and were driven off to our planes which were
Dakotas.   We loaded all our luggage on board and then waited.   After
about an hour I got out my great-coat and put it on as it was so
cold and there was a howling wind on the Airstrip.

Watched the Aircraft hands brushing the snow off the wings of
the Dakota and warming up the Engines.   The rumour then came round
that there would be no flying until 12 o'clock,- it was then about
9 o'clock and the sun was getting up nicely.   So I got out my gloves
which had got soaked the night before and tried to dry them on the
tail of the Dakota.

At about a quarter to twelve we were all beginning to feel very
hungry - but did not want to dig into our rations as we thought we
would need those on the journey.   We were told that a N.A.A.F.I.
van would be coming round at about 12 o'clock.

But just as the N.A.A.F.I. van came into sight, another lorry
came up and we were all told to pile into it and leave our baggage
behind.

We were driven off to the Customs Office, where we had our passports stamped and were asked if we had any Soap or letters of
Introduction to anybody on the Continent.

We then went into the next room where there was a W.A.A.F
serving tea and sandwiches, which we gobbled up.   We were all very
amused to see an article in the Sunday Dispatch saying that we had
flown over last night and landed in Germany.

We were then told that we would not be flying to-day as although the sun was shining over here there were storms on the Continent, and they were taking no chances as they had lost 2 Dakotas from this Airport within the last week; we all felt flattered about their care for our safety but rather depressed about the thought that we were not going to-day.

Managed to paint my initials on my kitbag to prevent it getting lost during movements and then went back to the Transit (Rover) Camp in the lorries.- Got back about 2 o'clock - several people went off into Cirencester - but I stayed and had a look round the Camp.

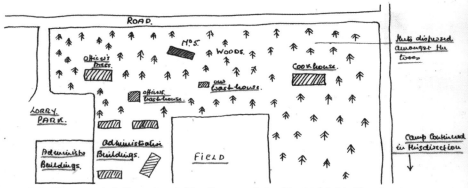

Got the general layout of the Camp and in the sunlight the Camp looked quite nice, it was set in the middle of a small wood and had concrete paths.

Eventually found that the officers' wash-house had hot water and so I wandered down and had a shave. Came back and started to re-adjust my equipment - decided to pack my haversack and belt into my pack and to wear my great-coat.

It now started to snow again - went down and had some tea at
the cookhouse, lounged around until 7 o'clock, then had supper and
went into the N.A.A.F.I. - had beer, bought some sheelaces and razor
blades and also some oranges and went back to the hut, to find
Ken Easton and Arthur Baines busy trying to get the fire going; they
had 3 attempts and failed, so then Dick Jenkins and David Bowler
had a go and managed to get it to go.

Spent the rest of the evening talking and went to bed at about
10 o'clock feeling extremely cold and none too hopeful of our chances
at getting off to-morrow.

We were told that we would have to get up again at 4.30 and that
breakfast would be at 5 o'clock.

MONDAY April 30th.

We were woken up at 4.30 a.m. by the cook, who sounded much too
cheerful, found that the fire which we had banked up the night before
was still in and by shoving a few sticks on it I was able to dress
in comparative warmth as my bed was next to the fire.

Had breakfast at 5 o'clock which consisted of the baked beans
which we were getting rather fed up with - got on the lorries -
Russel Barton was late but we all got aboard safely and started off.

We got to the Airport at about 6.30 and the weather looked good.
After a brief delay we were driven to our Aircraft and got our luggage
aboard.   After we had got it all aboard safely we were told that
we were in the wrong aircraft - so we put all our kit back onto the
lorry and were taken to another aircraft.

As we reached it a Dakota took off with one party of our chaps aboard. In our plane the pilot was already waiting and our gear was quickly stowed away - we were told to put on our Mae West life jackets and got into marvellous padded seats -(this was a transport plane reserved for Very Important People) - the engines roared up and we taxied onto the Runway.

The Control Van flashed a green light, the Engines roared up until we thought that they were bound to burst - then we began to taxi - got faster and faster and then we were off the ground. We did a climbing turn until we were about 1000 feet off the ground - then levelled out and flew South-East, as far as I could gather from the sun; We carried on flying for about an hour - with no idea of where we were. Looking down at the ground we noticed that the fields, which even at that time, 7.30 a.m., looked green, quite suddenly turned white and we realized that there was frost on the ground.

After another 5 minutes flying we began to run into dark, black cloud and the aircraft began to bump about a bit. We carried on flying through this for about 15 minutes and then the door at the front end of the aircraft opened and one of the crew poked his head through and said that they had received a wireless message to return, as the weather ahead was so bad. This was very disappointing but there was nothing we could do about it, we learnt afterwards that we got within sight of the English Channel! We landed at Croyden at about 9.45. We were shepherded into a room and told by an

Army officer that if we left it we would have to go through the Customs again
- so we sat in a waiting room and watched repatriated P.O.W's coming back.

At about 12 o'clock our 2 pilots arranged lunch for us in the R.A.F.
officers mess.   Of the 6 Aircraft, two had landed at Croyden, 2 had got
across the English Channel, 1 had turned back and landed at Down Aphny, and
1 had not taken off at all.   After quite a good lunch we took off again and
headed back towards Down Aphny.

The sun was well out and the countryside looked very nice - it took us
about 15 - 20 minutes to fly back to Down Aphny - when we arrived the lorries
were there and they took us to have tea and sandwiches again in the Refreshments
room, and then we drove back to the Camp.

Back at the Camp we heard that one plane had landed at Brussels and that
the other plane was missing and nothing had been heard from it.

Back at the Camp I got the fire going after several unsuccessful attempts
- had supper and then went round to the N.A.A.F.I. for half-an-hour.

Stoked up the fire and went to bed at 9.30 as I was feeling very tired.

TUESDAY May 1st.

We were woken up at 5 o'clock - found that the fire was out - had breakfast with the usual baked beans - packed up all our kit, we were getting rather
good at packing by this time, and scrambled onto the lorries to leave the Camp
about 6 o'clock.

On the way to the Airport we all admired the Army Motor-cyclist who guided
the convoy of six lorries - he was riding an open motor-cycle and only wearing

a 'Mac' while we were sitting in closed lorries wrapped up in greatcoats, scarves etc. and still we were cold, but he never looked cold and had a red, weather-beaten, cheery face in complete contrast to our cold, white, pinched and gloomy faces.

This time we were going to a different Airport - Blakehill Farm- because the Dakotas which had been held for us at Down Aphny had already waited 2 days and were now booked for another job.

Blakehill Farm was about 10 miles further on than Down Aphny - i.e. about 20 miles from the Transit Camp and when we arrived we realized that it was an R.C.A.F. Station and as well as the Canadians it was a Paratroop and Glider Station as well, because wandering all over the place were British Glider pilots.

After a short delay we drove onto the Airstrip and there we saw the huge Hamilcar Gliders we had all heard so much about. They all looked extremely flimsy and we were very glad that we were not Airborne troops.

We dismounted from our lorries and had a roll call taken. We were all present and the Movement Control officer said that we were due to fly at 12 o'clock as the Dakotas, in which we were to fly over, had to come from Croydon and had not arrived yet.

So we got back on our lorries and were driven off to the Sergeant's Mess - here we sat around and had tea until about 11.30 and then Tom Crisp from U.C.H - who had been a Captain in the Army and had the M.C. and Africa Star - said that as we had the rank of Red Cross Officers we were entitled to go in the Officers Mess, and as he had the M.C. and Africa Star his words carried some weight.

We all moved into the officers mess and sat around in armchairs asking every R.C.A.F. pilot we saw what were the chances of taking off to-day - they were all rather pessimistic and made us so also.

We had a good lunch in their mess and then after lunch a 'phone message came through saying that they were very sorry but the "Meds were scrubbed for to-day".

So we wandered out and got onto our lorries and were just about to move off when an officer came up and said that it was O.K. and we would be flying at 2 o'clock.

Wild excitement, and we drove onto the Airstrip again to find our planes all lined up with their engines running and the pilots at the controls.

We got off the lorries and began to get hold of our kit and move off towards the planes when the Movement Control Officer dashed up and said that the weather had got worse on the other side and we were again "scrubbed".

Drove back to the Rover Camp feeling very depressed and we were certainly not cheered up at the sight of the Camp, which we were beginning to hate.

Had tea and then had a shave - found that an R.A.F. convoy bound for the Far East was also sharing the camp with us.

Sat around in the evening talking with David Bowler and we decided that if we had to wait on the Airfield for more than half-an-hour we were not going that day.

We did not really expect to go to-morrow, as one of the pilots had said that the weather might continue as it was for a week.

Went to bed at 9.30 as we were feeling very tired, all the others were still out in Cirencester.

Still no news of the missing plane, but it was thought that it had landed safely

WEDNESDAY May 2nd.

We were woken up at 3.0 a.m. this morning, we all had the laugh on Ronnie Citrine, who, deciding that we were not going to-day, had only got into bed at 1.0 o'clock.

Had the usual breakfast - beans and bacon and left the Camp in lorries at 4.30 a.m. Got to Blakehill Faren at about 5.15 and were told that the weather was quite suitable and that we would be flying at 6 o'clock.

Packed all our kit into the plane and then got in - we had to rearrange the kit along the middle of the plane under the pilot's guidance - then the engines warmed up, a W.A.A.F. Nursing Orderly climbed in - the door was shut and bolted and we taxied onto the runaway - waited there for about 5 minutes and then took off to become Airborne at 6.30 a.m.

Again we flew S.E. and we managed to rearrange ourselves, we all had to go to the front of the aircraft while we took off, so that we each had a window to look out of.

We crossed England, which did not look very interesting as it was still asleep, and the sun had not yet risen and then in about an hour we sighted the English Channel; we had been told previously that it took about 10 minutes to fly the channel, so we carefully timed it, and it did - we did not know where we crossed the Coast on either side - but the Navigator said that we were heading towards Brussels, so we presumed that we were flying over Belgium - we were flying low about 1000 feet- so we could see the countryside well - occasionally we saw groups of bomb craters, but not very many of these.

We passed Lille and soon came within sight of Brussels - we did a half circle over Brussels Airport and then headed towards our destination - Celle in Germany.

We flew on steadily, noticing the increasing number of canals and

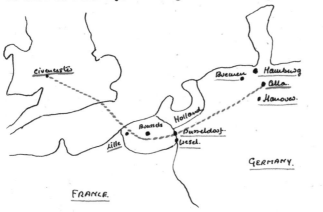

waterways and also how very much more regular the countryside was compared
with England.   We then came within sight of the Rhine, which had only been
crossed by our troops a short time previously - we could not see much activity,
though we could see several blown up bridges and several bridges which we had
built.   The Rhine had many bomb and shell craters on its banks.   We crossed
it at Wesel.

Now we were into Germany - the countryside did not look any different to
that of Belgium - but we did see Autobahmen. Gradually the countryside began
to get more wooded - we had passed over the Dortmund-Ems Canal but I did not
see it.

More flying - it was beginning to get a bit boring by now, and then the
navigator popped his head round the door and said that we would be landing at
Celle in half an hour.

As we came near the Airport we noticed a number of wrecked German Aircraft round the Perimeter - we circled and then landed - our ears buzzing and singing so that we could not hear each other speak.

When we got out of the plane the first thing that struck me was that everyone without exception was armed and looked very grim, and also the tremendous number of aircraft on the Airfield which was much smaller than Blakehill Faren.

We unloaded all our kit and collected near the Hangars.   Here we found all the others and we had our Allied Military Permits stamped with the date of our arrival.

As there was no telephonic communication with Belsen Camp a dispatch rider was sent off to ask for lorries to come and fetch us - the Camp was 18 miles away.   The time was now about 10.30 a.m. - at 2.30p.m., after we had been waiting on the Airport for 4 hours, the lorries arrived and we drove off through Celle to Belsen Concentration Camp.

We did not see many Germans en route as it was mostly through open country, but we did notice that the roads were appallingly bad, and that Germany looked much bleaker than England - the colours were not so rich.

We arrived at the Panzertruppen Schule, which was about 1 mile from the actual Concentration Camp, and had been used as barracks by the S.S. troops guarding the Concentration Camp.

We were shown our barracks and told that tea would be ready in the Officers Mess at 5 o'clock.   Began to get unpacked - we each had separate rooms (though in some cases two shared one room) and each room had a bed, wash basin, fire, table and chair and wardrobe.

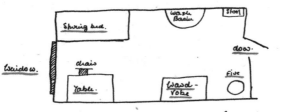

Lay out of my room in the Panzertruppen Schule.

Finished unpacking, made my bed up and then went down to the Mess to have tea. The Mess was a brick building with inlaid wooden beams, rather like our Tudor houses. Inside it was divided into 2 main rooms, 1 big room which was our mess, and 1 smaller room which was the regular Army Officers Mess, and in between them was the kitchen. We had a good tea with white bread, margarine and jam and we were waited on by Hungarian Army waiters.

After tea I went off with Lionel Garstin to the "Roundhouse", which was the Banquet - cum-Dance Hall of the Camp, to find a bed for him. We found 2 marvellous spring beds and then had a look round the Dance Hall.

Marvellous place about 75 yards long and 20 yards wide all panelled in light oak - with a musicians gallery and huge chandeliers from the ceiling.

There were several slashed photographs and paintings of Hitler and German Army generals. The tables in the hall were littered with glasses and bottles - all empty as both the liberating Tommies and the S.S. Guards before they left had drunk all they could. So we decided that we would examine the place more thoroughly to-morrow night and went back to our block (L.2) and set up our "liberated" spring beds.

Went down to the Mess and had a hot supper, and there we met Derek Wells
and George Woodwark, who had got across the channel on Monday, and had spent
27 hours in Brussels, and then flown on to Celle. Also Eric Wimmer, whose
pilot had taken them straight on to Celle - flying at 11,000 feet. They were
all so cold that they put on greatcoats, huddled together and had to go up
into the pilots cabin one at a time in order to get warm.

After supper we sat around in our rooms and talked and then turned into
bed to sleep our first night in Germany. We were told that we were going
to start work to-morrow, so far all we had learnt was that we were each going
to be given charge of a hut containing from 300 - 500 people.

THURSDAY May 3rd.

I was woken up at 7.0 a.m. and then went down to the Mess to have breakfast (bacon, porridge and tea). Noticed that all the walls of the German
Officers Mess were hung with English fox-hunting scenes!

After breakfast Dr. Meicklejohn, who was a Nutritional expert from the
School of Tropical Medicine and who was in charge of the Medical side of our
work, gave us a talk about the Concentration Camp and our work.

He said that the Concentration Camp used to be divided into 2 camps.

" Camp I - which contained about 50,000 people when it was liberated
(THE Belsen Concentration Camp) in which the conditions were extremely bad.

Camp II - which was situated at the top end of the Panzertruppenschule
and which contained about 15,000 people, mainly men - who were comparatively
fit and conditions were reasonably good.

There are at this moment about 27000 people in Camp I who are very badly
in need of all kinds of medical treatment.

The light Ack-Ack

The light Ack-Ack which were the first and only troops in the Camp
had established cookhouses in the Camp and they produced food - put it into
bins and then took the bins round and left them outside each hut - but that
there was no-one inside the huts to see that the food was fairly distributed
and that at the moment the fit people were getting all the food and the ill
people were not getting any.

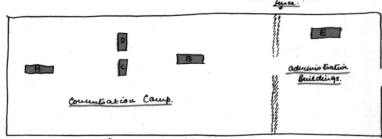

PLAN OF THE KITCHENS.

Our job was to see that the food was fairly distributed inside the huts
and to give any medical attention we could to the inmates.   Drugs in limited
quantities could be obtained from Woodwark and Wells who had set up a
dispensary on some liberated German stocks of drugs.

When we got to the Camp we were to be sprayed with D.D.T. and then go to
the Camp Office where we would each be allocated to a hut.

We all clambered onto the lorries which were going to take us to the
Camp and drove along an extremely bad road for about 1 mile until we came to
Camp I.

Here on the Main Gates was a red notice warning everyone that there was
Typhus in the Camp and another notice saying "Speed limit 10m.p.h. - Dust
Spreads Typhus".

We drove just inside the gates and then stopped. We then dismounted and joined a queue in order to be D.D.Td. While waiting we looked around the part of the Camp we could see. We had not been told that this was the administrative area of the Camp and therefore clean and so at our first sight of it the Camp did not look too bad.

We were then sprayed and walked along the main road through the Camp - until we came to the Camp Office. Here a Red Cross Woman Secretary (Mrs Crossthwaite)allotted huts to us.

I was allotted Hut I Laager I (Men) - located the hut on the map of the Camp and then set off to find it.

I now began to see the Concentration Camp proper, the first thing that struck me was the amazing bleakness of the Camp - the huts had once been painted red - but this had faded to an indiscriminate pink - and otherwise there was no colour at all in the Camp, everything was grey or slaty brown. The next thing was the dust, this was everywhere and even as you walked you left clouds of dust behind you.

Then the Internees - they looked thin, brown and dirty and they shuffled along in a purposeless sort of way, dressed in their blue and white striped slave clothing. They were not in the least interested in anything and took no notice of us at all as we walked by.

Found my hut after some difficulty, but on going inside with Russell Barton who was also sharing the hut, we found that it was comparatively clean - that it contained 3-tier bunks and that all the men inside it seemed capable of walking, and therefore capable of getting their own food and eating it.

So we reported back to the Office and we were told to try Hut 224
Laager I (Women).   We found by looking at the map that this was right at
the other end of the Camp.   We set off towards it and noticed another striking
thing about the Camp - the Smell - this was a hot, humid smell mixed up with
the smell of burning boots, dirty clothing and faeces and once smelt was never
forgotten!

Another thing was the very tall barbed wire fences about 15 feet high
and the huge Watch Towers, strung along the fences at about 200 yards intervals
and rising to a height of about 40 feet and then between the Watch Towers were
stretched powerful Electric Arc lights.

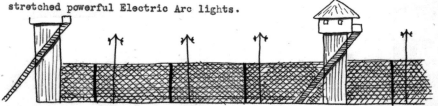

We eventually came into the Women's Laager, where the Smell increased in
intensity - we found Hut 224, which was painted the usual pink colour with the
Red Cross which the Germans had had the nerve to paint on each hut.

We went into the hut and were almost knocked back by the smell, but we
went into one of the two main rooms.

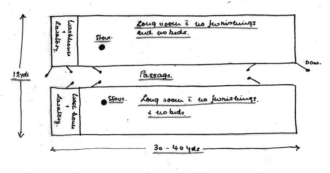

HUT 224.

The sight that met us was shocking - there were no beds whatsoever and in this one room there were about 200 people lying on the floor. In some cases they wore a few battered rags and in some cases they wore no clothes at all.

They were all huddled together one next to the other. In many cases 1 blanket having to cover 3 people. The floor was covered in faeces and soaked in urine and the people lying on the floor were in just the same state - as they all had extremely severe diarrhoea and were all too weak to move.

Next to each person was a tin can or old mug and various small pieces of bread which they were carefully hoarding up - this latter lying on the floor and when they felt like it they took a bite out of it - irrespective of what it had been lying in. Their hair, hands, faces and feet were all covered in a mixture of dry faeces and dirt. At least $\frac{3}{4}$ of them had hacking coughs and the other $\frac{1}{4}$ were just lying. Here and there a dead person could be seen lying between two living ones, who took no notice of her at all and just went on eating, coughing or just lying, and these were all women whose ages varied from 15-30.

We had a look at one or two patients and they were quite literally just a mass of skin and bones, with sunken eyes which had a completely vacant look. They all had bites and severe scabies and some had terrible ulcers and bedsores the size of small saucers, with no dressings on them at all.

We left them and went back to the other end of the room, followed by weak cries, or at least whines of "Herr Doktor, Herr Doktor", here we met a student from U.C.H. who said that he and another student had the Hut and were able to cope with it all right - we doubted this, but at that moment an Artillery Cookhouse Captain came up and said that there were no students in either Hut 222 or 210, so I went to 210 and Russell Barton to 222.

Went to Hut 210 and to my relief found that on Monday it had been cleaned out by the Hungarians and equipped with double tier bunks. There was a young Polish woman doctor in charge of it and under her were 6 polish women nurses.

Found that one of the nurses spoke quite good English and so I explained that Bill Clarke from Barts. and I were the doctors in charge of this hut. Then got the nurse and the Polish woman doctor ot show us round.

The floor of the hut was clean and the hut was divided up into seven rooms in one of these lived the doctor and nurses and the others were divided up into wards, and these wards were used for Typhus, post Typhus and Advanced Tuberculosis. She had all her patients fairly well seperated into these groups, though there were some in the wrong wards.

There were about 40 people to each room and they were lying, 2 to a bunk i.e. 4 people to each double tiered bunk which was hopeless overcrowding.

Learnt that there were about 260 people in the hut

<u>Hut 210.</u>

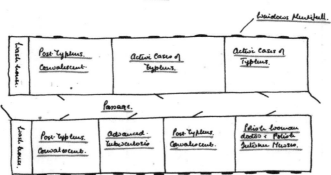

and that every single one, including the doctor, had either had Typhus or was having it now.

Went round one ward putting a G on the bed of each patient who ought to have Glucose Solution with Vitamins. Asked for a list of all the patients in the hut - with their age and nationality by to-morrow morning. Then went and had lunch.

In the afternoon went to the office and indented for 2 dead to be taken away. Collected 2 Hungarians and went down to the Cookhouse to see if I could get some Glucose Solution - found that they had run out of Glucose, but I managed to collect a tin of biscuits - got some Glucose later.

Came back to 210 to find that the Cookhouse Captain had left some Ovaltine, Horlicks, Cocoa and slabs of chocolate. Mixed Ovaltine, Horlicks and Cocoa together. Made it up and managed to give a cupfull of that, 2 cupfulls of Glucose Solution, 1 biscuit and 1 square of chocolate to each patient about 240 of them. They were all very grateful.

By this time it was about 5.30 so made out my returns for the hut,

                    Total = 260)
                    Sick = 240) from Polish doctor and Nurse.
                    Dead = 2)

and handed them in to Mrs Crossthwaite - then hitched a lift back to Camp II. Got back at 6.30 in time for Dr. Meiklejohns' Conference. It was decided that more Glucose should be produced the next day, that the Opium consumption would have to be cut down. Had supper.

Went up to L.2. and then with Ronnie Citrine and Russell Barton went to the Roundhouse - to find that it was being cleared out in order to turn it into a Hospital, so we did not find anything to "liberate".

Came back and talked until 11 o'clock and then went to bed.

FRIDAY May 4th.

Woken up at 7.30 a.m. - dressed and went down to breakfast at 7.45.
After breakfast there was another Conference - nothing new was decided upon
and so I hitched a lift on an Artillery limber to Camp I.   Collected 2
Hungarian soldiers from outside the office and marched off down to 210.   They
told me that there had been 2 deaths during the night - one of them had been a
Typhus case.

They had the list of patients ready and so I asked the Polish woman doctor
to come round with me and explain what each patient had.   First of all set the
2 Hungarians to work washing all the floors.

The Polish doctor seemed quite competent - knew all her patients by name
and the diagnosis in each case.   Saw 18 cases of active Typhus which had rashes
and many more, who she said had Typhus and though all I could see was that
they had a fever I had to take her word for it, as since she had been in the
Camp, she had treated many hundreds of cases of Typhus and had also had the
disease herself.   Learnt that two of the Complications of Typhus were
Myocardial degeneration and stiff joints.

There were many cases of Oedema in patients who had no other signs of
Cardiac failure and who appeared to be able to eat alright - diarrhoea was
prevalent everywhere and I had to tell her that she could only give $\frac{1}{2}$ Tablet
($\frac{1}{4}$ grain) of opium to those with severe diarrhoea as we were running short of
Opium.   I was not very popular with her after this.

In the Tubercle Ward, the tuberculosis was very advanced, they all had
very bad coughs, and several had quite bad Haemoptysis - they were all very
thin and emaciated but whether this was due to Tuberculosis or starvation I
could not tell, there was nothing we could do for them except to give them
Opium to relieve both their cough and their diarrhoea - neither of which it

helped to any considerable extent.

Managed to get through all the patients by lunch time and so went off to lunch.   At lunch Mr. de Greefe (our Welfare Officer) said that some different arrangement would have to be made about transport, as 3 lorries had turned up after breakfast and only 5 people were there waiting to go to Camp I, as all the rest had hitched-hiked, so it was decided that we would all 'hitch' to and from Camp I and there would be no regular transport.

After lunch I went down to Kitchen H which was the invalid kitchen and collected a large 8 gallon can of Glucose and vitamin mixture.   Went back to the hut and gave out the Glucose to about 204 patients - so far they seemed to have tolerated yesterday's glucose quite well, though one or two had vomited it. The people who had Typhus did not like it as it was too sweet for them and they kept on asking for "Lemon" but we had no lemon flavouring of any sort in the Camp.

Went round the wards looking at some of the cases.   There was 1 girl who had a sore throat, inflamed fauces, sore mouth and lips and pain in the ears. Could not see any membrane anywhere, so diagnosed pharyngitis, but thought that it might be diphtheria.   Gave her 10gr Aspirin as she had a slight fever, and gave her 3 grammes of Sulphathiazole stat with a dosage of 1 gramme 4 hourly until the next morning - told the nurse to see that she drank plenty of water and tea.

I enquired into the food situation and found that they all liked potatoes and tea, but they did not like the brown bread, unless they had something to spread on it, personally I don't blame them as each loaf weighed about a ton and was only half baked.

Came back to the Camp and had supper.   After supper an R.A.M.C.
Lieut/Colonel gave us a talk on the clinical aspect of Typhus - it was very
good and much appreciated.   He was interrupted in the middle to say that
the Germans opposite the 21st Army Group had surrendered - all very pleased.
We were then told that there would be a salute fired by the Ack-Ack to-morrow
morning at 8 o'clock.   Sat around in the Mess until about 11.30 and then
went up to L.2. and crawled into bed.

    Returns from 210:   Total = 208)
                          Sick = 178) from list of patients
                          dead = 2.)

Had a look at the "death Squad" to-day - this consisted of a cart drawn
by a lorry and on the cart are about eight German Prisoners of War - they are
dressed in protective Anti-gas clothing and their job is to go round the Camp,
under the orders of armed British Guards, and calling at each hut collect all
the dead and then take them away in the cart to be buried elsewhere - now with
a proper burial service.

    These men have replaced the S.S. men who had to do the carting and burying
of the dead at the bayonet point, when we first liberated the Camp.

SATURDAY May 5th.

    Up at 7.15 - breakfast at 7.45.   Got a rotten cold and feel lousy -
several chaps are down with diarrhoea and vomiting.   There was the usual after
breakfast discussion - in which I and several other people brought up the
question of white bread, and Meicklejohn said that he would see what could be
done about it, - it was decided that more glucose would be produced to-day
 - though it would be less than yesterday, only 1000 litres - hopelessly
inadequate amount.

Got up to the Camp and realized just how cold it was.   Went to 210 after
first collecting 2 Hungies - told them to fetch water - then asked the nurses
and doctor if they had heard the Gunfire - they had, and when I told them
that the Germans in the North had surrendered, they just were not interested,
smiled politely and that was all!

I decided that there was not enough work for me to do in 210 and that
they would be able to manage on their own as the Polish doctor was quite competent.

So I went up to the Office and asked Mrs Crossthwaite if there were any
huts without any students in them.   She said that there were plenty and told
me to try 211.   Went down there but found that 211 was being cleaned out,
preparatory to being made into a Hospital - so went back and was given Hut 217.
Went and had a look at it and decided that I was definitely needed there.

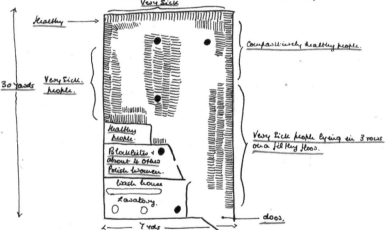

217 was a smaller hut than the others - 30yds x 7yds but it contained
about 460 women.   I walked in and it was easily the most crowded hut I had
yet seen.   The first thing I did was to yell above the din and ask if anyone
spoke English; fortunately one of the fairly fit people spoke quite reasonable
English - told her that I wanted a list of all the very sick people by after

lunch including their ages.

Then I had a look round the Hut, it was composed of 1 single large room with people, lying, sitting and standing all round the walls and also in the centre of the Hut, most of the people who were very sick, were lying opposite the door and along the right wall of the hut.   They were lying in roughly three rows, but they were all packed together head to foot so that there was absolutely no room whatsoever in between the rows.

The amazing thing about the Hut was the people who were fit, there must have been at least 200 fit, almost fat, well people in the hut, and yet they were content to stay there in the hut, living in those filthy, stuffy cond ditions, rather than move into some of the huts which were clean and half empty.   The sick were arranged in 3 main groups according to the diagram. Decided that there was nothing to be done until after lunch when I would be able to get drugs and bandages from the dispensary and glucose from the kitchen.

After lunch I collected these and made my way down to the Hut. Collected the glucose and then started to give it out - 1 cupful to each person - had heard at lunch that about $\frac{3}{4}$ of the people to whom I had given Glucose yesterday had vomited it, so I was not too happy about giving it out to-day - but the patients seemed to like it and as there was no other form of fluid food available and they could not eat bread, there was nothing else for it.

After this I went round all those who had very severe diarrhoea and gave them $\frac{1}{2}$ opium tablet each, and then gave out aspirin to those who had post-Typhus joints, pains and headaches etc., as I considered it more efficient in relieving pain than the Opium tablets.

Gave 2 Vitamins each to the 98 worst sick, Opium to 50, and Aspirin 15 gr. to 20 people.

Captain Peters - the R.A.M.C. Captain who was in charge of evacuating the worst huts, came round and had a look at the hut.   He said that next to 216, which was George Woodwark's hut which had already had 200 sick evacuated, and was still the first priority hut to have 100 more evacuated, mine was the worst hut and he would take 90 of my worst cases to-morrow.

Treated what appeared to be a tonsillitis with 2 grammes Stat Sulpha-thiazole and then 1 gramme 2 hourly for 8 hours, told my interpreter - nurse, who was called Raja, to see that she drank plenty of water - did some dressing of various ulcers and bedsores and what appeared to be two discharging sinuses communicating with the hip joint - thought that they were probably Tuberculous.

Opened a Breast abscess with a razor blade heated in a flame and then cooled in alcohol.   Made a quick 2 inch incision and then packed it with flavine gauze - no anaesthetic and patient must have been in great agony - but she did not yell and before I left the hut all the pain from the abscess had gone and she was feeling much better.   Opened a boil on the forearm in a similar way - there is another woman who has a large abscess under her jaw which will have to be opened soon, but as it is not ready yet and she is one of the ones to be evacuated to-morrow, I left it hoping that they will do it under better conditions at the Hospital in Camp II.
It was now about 6 o'clock and I thought that as 216 was just next to mine and was the worst hut in the camp I would go across and look at it.

George Woodwark was there and showed me round and it certainly was the worst.   In many places whole gaps of the floor were missing and you squelched down onto earth and God only knows what else - it was hopelessly overcrowded and faeces were even more abundant than in the other huts.   George said that they had pulled several bodies out from under what floorboards were left, and I could quite well believe it.   Was jolly glad to get out into the ? fresh air again.

Came back to Camp II and had quite a good supper and some Hock which an R.A.F. Padre had sent us.   After supper a Polish band came and played to us outside the Officers Mess - they were pretty awful but it was a spontaneous gesture and was much appreciated.   We are all beginning to get very behind hand with the news and have very little idea what is happening in the war except that we are doing well.

Went up to L.2. wrote a letter, still got my cold and so I went to bed at about 10.30.

Hut returns from 217

      Total = 400)
      V.Sick= 98)   obtained from my Interpreter-nurse.
      Sick = 198)
      Dead = 2.)

SUNDAY May 6th.

Up at 7.15 - breakfast - had the usual Conference after breakfast but nothing of any value came out of it.   Went to the Camp and collected 2 Hungarians but found that I had to sign for them - regular Trades Union starting up!

Went to 217 - it was raining and the Camp looked even more bleak than usual, it was also very cold.   Got the 2 Hungies to fetch water and then sweep the exposed part of the floor of the hut, and after that wash it.

Started to clear the spaces in between the sick but I found that this was a
Herculean task and well nigh impossible, as they were so close together, the
floor was so filthy and whatever dirty old rag or tin can which one took away
was somebody's prize possession, so I had to give it up.

It really is amazing how the fit will stay in 217 which is filthy rather
than go to 220 which is clean and almost empty, just across the way - just
suggested that they might do so and they all almost fainted at the idea.

The Ambulances which were going to take away the sick did not do so, as
there was no water in the "Human Laundry". Very great disappointment in the
Hut - 3 dead to-day.

Went round giving opium and aspirin to those who were very ill, and had
a look at and dressed a woman who had gangrene of both her little toes
(L) dry with a clear, well-marked line of seperation and (R) moist and line
of demarcation well marked again - dressed both with dry dressings and gave
her 20gr. aspirin for the pain.

Breast abscess is draining well and is not giving her any pain. Opened
another boil with the same technique. Dressed many ulcers and bedsores with
Ung. Hyd. Ammon. Some of the people here are very, very ill.

Roughly diagnosed 2 ? pneumonias - dull at the base with bronchial
breathing and fever - started them on Sulphathiazole - 2 grammes Stat. 1 gramme
2 hourly for 6 hours and then 1 gramme 4 hourly with fluids + +. The ?
Tonsillitis I treated is much better to-day and is walking around quite
happily and her tonsils seem to be getting smaller, or is it just the eye of
faith!

There appears to be quite a lot of scurvy - (bleeding gums - teeth bad and falling out - sore tongue) doled out 8 army compound Vitamin Tablets. to each

Some "Bengal Mixture" arrived - this was a form of gruel which was used with success in the Bengal Famine, and was made up of sugar, salt, flour, oatmeal etc. - but there was too much sugar in it and they would not touch it. Went back and had lunch & after lunch we all complained to Meiklejohn about the "Bengal Mixture" and told him that it was too sweet - as the sugar was the thing which we were trying to get into them, it was thought that it might be alright to reduce the sugar by half and increase the amount of salt.

Went back to the hut and carried on doing the dressings, there were hosts to be done, managed to do about ¼ of them - found 2 cases of tender enlarged, apparently not inflamed, lumps in the Axilla - could'nt think what they were so just put a dry dressing on them and gave them the usual Aspirin for their pain.

About half way through the afternoon, an R.A.M.C. Captain came in and photographed the hut, stayed and chatted for a few minutes. Carried on with the dressings, and then an American doctor, an English Army Nursing Sister and a Red Cross nurse came and had a look at the hut. Showed them round and made a point of showing them all the worst cases I could - when we came to the end they left rapidly without even saying Thank - you.

Found that another woman had died - she was in a very bad way and I expected her to die - advanced T.B. I think.

Went back to Camp II and almost had to walk back as I was so late, but eventually hitched a lift.

We were each given a camouflaged Panzer coat - we had all wanted one of these since the day we got out here - they were a present from Captain Winterbottom and we were all very grateful.

Had my first bath in Germany - the bathhouse was a seperate building containing about 40 baths, each bath was in a tiled cubicle of its own and completely private.   The baths were built in and there were mirrors for shaving, so it was like 40 bathrooms in one building.

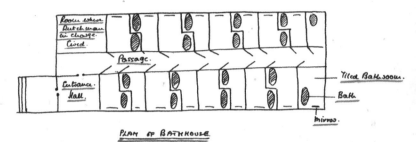

PLAN OF BATHHOUSE.

There was a Dutchman in charge and he showed us in, clicked his heels and ran our water for us - much singing, came back to bed after a good day's work.
Returns from 217.

```
        Total = 350  )
        Ill   = 150  )
        Well  = 200  )      my counting.
        Very ill = 98)
        dead     = 4 )
```

Rumour that we may have to move into tents.

MONDAY May 7th.

Up at 7.15 - breakfast at 7.45 - usual conference after breakfast - went to Camp I and collected 100 Tanalbin tablets from the dispensary - this was a cure for diarrhoea acting on its Tannic Acid Content - reports about its use were varied, some said it was no use and some said that it was good.

Went to 217 and found that my Hungarians had not turned up, so went back - stormed into the Hungarian Commander's office - swore at him in English and kept on saying "Zwei Hungarian" - he promptly stood up and saluted - gave an order and up came 2 Hungarians, and I walked off with them.

Then did a ward round of my hut.   On the whole they appeared much better

and in some cases the diarrhoea had stopped - though many cases still needed

urgent treatment.ꞯ Oedema ┼ ┼ was everywhere.

Sought out Captain Peters and the light field Ambulance and found out that

they were willing to evacuate 100 sick cases after they had taken 100 sick

from 216.   Was asked to mark those I wanted to have evacuated, so that only

those who were meant to go should get onto the stretchers, as they had found

that whenever they put a stretcher on the floor, all the fit people near it

would promptly get onto it!

Went round and marked them with Tb, Ec. and F. (Enteric and Famine

Oedema) - I marked about 81 of my most sick people in this way.

Found that the commonest symptoms were:

(1) Diarrhoea - Very bad with prostration

(11)Fever, with severe loss of appetite and cough

(111) Oedema - of feet, legs, hands and in some cases face.   Somehow I do

not think that this Oedema is entirely due to famine, as in many cases they

could walk and eat.   On questioning I found that almost every case had had

Typhus and so ¹ wondered whether it might be due to temporary cardiac weakness

following on the cardiac lesions of Typhus, but I could not see any distended

neck veins and the heart sounds seemed to be normal.

The gruel came round again to-day but it was both too sweet, too salt

and was also burnt and so the patients again would not eat - if they have

any more disappointments with it they will not eat it even if it is well made.

Came back to my hut at 1.30 and found that the Ambulance people were

already starting to evacuate the hut - had given orders to Raja before lunch

that all those who were marked must be stripped and so stripped of all clothes they were put onto stretchers, wrapped in blankets and then carried into the Ambulances to start a new life with no clothes or possessions of any kind, all these being taken outside, when they had gone, and burnt.

From 217 they were taken to the 'Human Laundry' in Camp II.

German nurses, 4 to each patient washing & D.D.T.'ing each patient

Patients out to the Hospital in Camp II

Patients IN from Camp I

clean Blankets.   clean Stretchers.   clean Stretchers.   clean Blankets

Motor plant for heating water

THE HUMAN LAUNDRY.

This consisted of 2 German stables equipped with tables and with hot water - there were 4 German nurses to each table and they washed the patients all over with soap and water and then their hair was clipped short and they were sprayed with D.D.T. then wrapped in clean blankets, put into clean Ambulances and then taken off to the Hospital in Camp II.

This "Human Laundry" was a pretty good trial for the patients as it is not funny to have soap rubbed into a painful ulcer.

11 of the German Nurses have gone down with Typhus!

When I got back to my hut, I found that my hut was almost completely cleared of sick and I set my Hungies to work to clear the Hut of all their clothing etc.

I had lost some very interesting cases and I was sorry to see them go - but they will be better off in Camp II.   There was one very interesting case of a unilateral cyst of the (R) Eyelid, also my breast abscesses, and my 2 T.B. Hip Sinuses.

Soft superficial translucent cyst.

I was invited to tea by my blockleiter -

did not want to go but thought that it would be good policy to have it.
Found out that the majority of the Poles had been there in Belsen since
January and that before that they had been in Auschwitz, and that previous
to January '45 conditions had not been so bad at Belsen.

Came back for supper and learnt that it was V-E day.   Had Rum-punch to
celebrate it and then we had a sing-song.   1 chap from U.C.H. recited the
whole of Eskimo Nell - amazing performance, and so to bed.

Returns from 217.

                    Total = 315.)
                    Sick = 15.)   Includes those who slept in the hut but did
                    Fit   = 300)   not stay there during the day.
                    Dead = None

TUESDAY May 8th.

Up at 7.15, breakfast as usual, and by cutting the after breakfast
discussion managed to get to the Camp by 8.30.   Collected my 2 Hungies and
went down to 217.   En route watched a bull-dozer burying a huge pile of
barbed wire which it had knocked down.

Got quite a shock when I went into the Hut, as during the night from
absolutely nowhere the fit had managed to collect about 20 bunks and bring
them into the Hut - and they all looked as pleased as punch about it.

'Comforts' arrived from the kitchen - consisting of cigarettes and tinned
food, saw to the distribution of both these and also the food, which arrived at
the same time.   Really there was no need for me to do so because Rosa, the
blockleiter, was honest and had all the hut subdivided into sections, in fact
she had it all taped.

Did a ward round but as nearly all my sick had gone yesterday there was
not very much for me to do.

Raja said that Zosia who was a sort of deputy-blockleiter, and was quite
pretty wanted to learn English.   I was only too pleased to oblige, and so I

wrote out about 100 English words and Raja wrote out the Polish for them and
then I showed Zosia how to pronounce them and she wrote in the pronounciation
above them phoenetically - she was keen to learn and picked it up quickly.

Had lunch, and after lunch set the Hungies on to rearranging the beds
which the internees had brought in and just put down anywhere.   Managed to get
the hut looking quite neat and clean.

Was invited to tea again and had Herrings on biscuit - all out of a tin
thank heavens and some lukewarm tea.   Carried on teaching Zosia English still
by writing out the words and letting her learn them - finds the greatest
difficulty in saying any word with -th in it.

Got back to the Camp and learnt that to-day was the official V-E day.
We had Hock for dinner - then went into the other Officer's Mess where they
had a wireless and listened to the King's Speech.

The Colonel and his officers from 102 Control Section and some
Royal Artillery officers, the Ack-Ack had fired off another Salute to-day,
came in and joined us in a Sing-Song - again Eskimo Nell - had a Padre sitting
beside me!!!

The Colonel gave a short speech and explained how he had been a P.O.W.
for 2 years - and explained to us how, if you were behind barbed wire fences,
you felt that you only had to get to the other side of the wire and you were
free, and asked us to try and see the internees point of view in their desire
to get outside the wire in CampI - good speech.

Did not hear Churchill's speech - great pity as I should very much like
to have heard it.   We were all very sorry that we were not able to celebrate
the peace in England - which seemed a long way off.

More singing and then we all rolled into bed feeling very drunk.

Returns, Hut 217.

Total = 315
Fit   = 300
Sick = 15
Dead = None

WEDNESDAY May 9th.

Up at 7.15 - breakfast - cut the Conference and got to the Camp by 8.30.
Collected my two Hungarians - the system of signing for them seems to have
fallen through and we just walk up and collect them now.   Went to 217.

There seemed to be quite a busy air about the place and I was told by
Rosa (the Blockleiter), that over 200 of the fit people in the hut were going to
be evacuated to Camp IV at 2 o'clock to-day - this was the first that I had
heard about it and was inclined not to believe it.

So I supervised the cleaning of the hut and the distribution of food and
cigarettes - more Comforts (cigarettes and Tinned food) arrived for the inmates
towards the end of the morning.

Carried on teaching Zosia English - quite amazing the amount she has
picked up - she has learnt all the words that I wrote down for her yesterday,
and two days ago the only English word she could say was "please".   Wrote out
some more words and also some Verbs and Sentences, was quite surprised at my
lack of knowledge of English Grammar!

After lunch wandered back to the Hut, thinking of nothing in particular -
when suddenly I heard a chorus of voices saying "Auf Wiedersehn Doktor" -
looked up and saw about 250 people from my hut staggering along the road,
carrying all their worldly possessions wrapped up in blankets, on their way to
be sprayed with D.D.T. before going off to Camp IV - damned silly as half of
them will collapse when they get there and only clog up Camp IV (which is

meant for fit people) with sick.

Set the Hungarians to work, completely clearing the hut of old bedding and clothes in quite a short time.

I found that Rosa, Raja and Zosia and about 60 other people had remained behind - no reason except they thought that they would like to go to-morrow instead of to-day.

Had no work to do that afternoon, so I continued to give Zosia her English lessons. She has learnt so quickly that by speaking slowly and clearly I carry on a conversation with her. Proudly showed off my teaching results to Ronnie Citrine, who speaking in a normal way was completely unintelligible to her!

Stayed and had tea with them and then went back to CampII. Got back at 6.15 just in time to hear Colonel Johnstone, who was i/c of No.32 c.c.s. talking to us about the Concentration Camp.

He said that he and his men when they first came into the Camp found "A very great number of dazed, apathetic Human Scarecrows wandering around the Camp in a completely aimless fashion, dressed in rags and some even without rags - there were piles of dead everywhere right up to the front gate."

He said that when they arrived in the Camp they asked the Polish Women doctors for an estimate of the number of sick people in the Camp who needed Hospital attention and they said about 2000 - the figure as it stands to-day is 17,000.

He also explained the overall policy behind the Evacuation of the Concentration Camp.

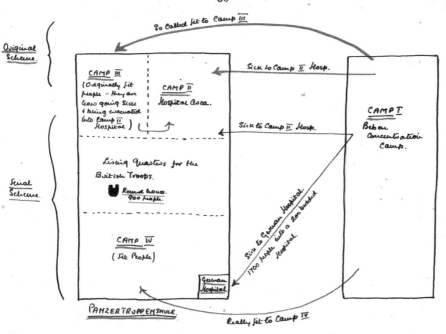

So called fit to Camp III

Original Scheme.

CAMP III
(Originally fit people – they are now going sick & being evacuated into Camp II Hospital)

CAMP II
Hospital Area.

Sick to Camp II Hosp.

CAMP I
Belsen Concentration Camp.

Sick to Camp II Hosp.

Final Scheme.

Living Quarters for the British Troops.
Round house. 900 people.

Sick to German Hospital. 1700 people into a 200 bedded Hospital.

CAMP IV
(Fit People)

German Hospital

PANZERTRUPPENSCHULE.

Really fit to Camp IV

EVACUATION OF BELSEN CONCENTRATION CAMP.

It was decided as soon as we came into the camp that Camp I would have to be evacuated into the Panzertruppenschule and so the top of the Panzer - Schule was divided into two (Camps II and III) Camp I being the Concentration Camp.

The so-called fit people were to go into Camp III the standard of fitness being anyone who could clamber up the two steps onto a lorry with assistance from a Tommy.

The sick people were to go into Camp II - where droves of Hungarians were at work throwing all the furniture from the barracks out of the windows and then putting in beds with palliases. They were only 2 buildings ahead of the patients coming in. In this way a Hospital was built up in Camp II at the rate of 500-700 beds a day.

This original Scheme broke down - owing to the fact that the "fit" people in Camp III were going down like flies and Camp III was rapidly beginning to resemble Camp I.

So they had to stop evacuating sick from Camp I and evacuate them instead from Camp III to Camp II.

After that the standard of fitness was raised slightly and instead of evacuating them into Camp III they created a new camp at the bottom end of the Panzer Schule - Camp IV and evacuated the fit people into that.

He said that the major crime of the Germans was to evacuate people from other camps (Auschwitz) into Belsen when they knew that Typhus was already raging in Belsen.

He also said that, although he had protested, 10 of the S.S. guards, who had contracted Typhus, had been sent from Celle to his Hospital - so he put them in his largest male ward, walked into the middle of it, announced that they were S.S. Guards and then walked out again.

The Rum Ration was started to-night and de Greefe managed to bring back 1000 bottles of beer from Hanover.   And so to bed.

> Zofia Wis'niowska   (77456)
>   Krakow
>   Plac Matejki 9,F
>   Polska.

Hut Returns = 60 fit people.

Learnt to-day from Raja that Zosia and her husband had run a resistance movement in Poland, that they had been captured $2\frac{1}{2}$ years ago and sent to Auschwitz and there they had been seperated - she also has a boy aged 5.

THURSDAY May 10th.

Up at 7.15 - breakfast but no conference and so I got to Camp I by 8.30 again - collected my Hungarians and set them to work clearing the remainder of the inside of 217 and also clearing all the filth which had been chucked out of the windows. Decided that there was not enough work for me to do in 217, so I went up to Hut 197 and gave Dick Jenkins a hand, treating the sick in his hut.

All the people in his hut were in treble tier bunks which was quite a help. He was still faced with the problem of diarrhoea - tried them on a Tanalbin dosage of 5 Tablets Stat then 2 tablets 2 hourly for 8 hours and in some cases 1½ gr. tablet of Opium.

Diagnosed 2 cases of Typhus - Fever, headache loss of appetite, suffused appearance and they had not had Typhus. Could not see any lice on them, but did not look too carefully.

Went back to 217 in time to stop Raja, Zosia and co from being evacuated, as they were willing to work and I had learnt from Tom Crisp that 217 was going to become part of the Hospital Area. They were a little doubtful about nursing and so I told them to think it over.

After lunch I gave Dick Jenkins a hand again, it was extremely hot in the hut and there was an overpowering smell of sweltering bodies and faeces; did some dressings and treated more diarrhoea - one case of cholecystitis and a case of recurrent appendicitis - several boils and one gangrene of the lower lip ? Cancrum Oris.

Went back to 217 at 5 o'clock and found that they were willing to stay providing that all 12 of them could stay on. I was not sure whether I would be allowed to keep as many as this and told them so - so then they said that they would leave. Laid it on thick about the nobleness of nursing and the saving of life etc. and then left them to think it over for the night.

Came back for supper and we had beer and rum: Afterwards I went up to the Cinema and saw "Greenwich Village": for a Garrison Cinema, the Germans had certainly built a marvellous place - like a West End Cinema except that their seats were wooden and not plush.

Came back to the mess and found out from Tom Crisp that I would be allowed to keep 12 people on as nurses, when 217 became a Hospital.

Hut returns ≟ 12 fit people - the other 50 had been evacuated during the afternoon.

And so to bed.

_____

FRIDAY May 11th.

Up 4 times during the night with diarrhoea, thought that I would have to report sick for the day - but found that I was not feeling so bad when the morning came.

At breakfast found that there were about 60 people who had had severe diarrhoea in the night - it was traced back to some meat we had eaten at supper.

Went to the Camp and collected 3 Hungies for 197 and 2 for 217. Set the ones in 217 to work clearing the small room (washroom), which was in a filthy state.

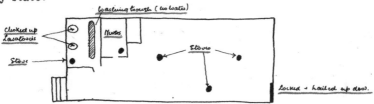

Told Raja and Zosia and Co. that 12 of them would be allowed to stay on in the hut - they all seemed quite pleased.

Then went up to hut 197 to help Dick - found that the Tanalbin had not had much effect upon the diarrhoea; possibly the dosage was not high enough, so stepped it up to 3 tablets every 2 hours.

Found several lice on one of the women, who I think has got Typhus, but as yet I could not see any petechiae.   Dropped some D.D.T. onto the lice and this killed them in about 1½ minutes - gave her a couple of handfulls of D.D.T. to rub into herself and then sprinkled some on her blankets - that should kill all the lice.

a louse

Went back to 217 and found that Raja was still in bed complaining that she had a "weak heart" and would I give her some "coramine".   I had refused to do so yesterday and I refused to do so to-day.

Came back to the hut after lunch, though really it was my afternoon off: Collected a tin of D.D.T. and then threw handfuls of it all over the hut - that ought to kill all the lice in the hut.

Raja came and said that she did not want to stay on and nurse but wanted to go to Bergen (Camp III), as we had been told that the conditions in Camp III were bad, I warned her about it, but she still wanted to go and so I let her go as she was very lazy and I do not think that she will like Camp III very much - the trouble is that she can speak English and also she is taking 7 of the other nurses with her, so that now I am only left with 5 nurses to look after any patients which may come in.

Spent the rest of the afternoon teaching Zosia English, she still learns quickly and can carry on quite a good conversation.   My grammar is definitely not so hot!

Came back to Camp II, had our photographs taken by a Movie Cameraman who was making a film about Belsen.   He photographed us at a conference with de Greefe lecturing to us.

Brigadier Glynn-Hughes R.A.M.C. S.M.O. 2nd Army came to dinner and afterwards talked to us about Belsen.

He gave us an account of how when conditions got completely out of hand in Belsen, the Germans decided to pass on the baby to us, and so they asked us to take over the Camp. We agreed providing that we also had an Area round the camp and that the bridges over a nearby river were left intact.

This latter the Germans refused to do and so it was decided to fight for the bridges - but it was agreed that there should be no firing into or out of the Area round the Camp which they were going to give up.

This worked in practice although a few shells did land in the area. There was no actual fighting in the area, though the Germans did not completely evacuate it.

It was agreed that all the Administrative Officers were to stay on in the Camp and also the German guards, who would then be given safe transport back to their own lines.

.From German Sources we gathered that the political (Waffen) S.S. were in charge of the Camp and they handed the Camp over to us on April 13th at 1200 hours, leaving only administrative officers and introducing Wehrhmacht Guards. We arrived on the afternoon of April 15th.

Brigadier Glynn-Hughes was the first man to enter the Camp, and he was followed by one battery of Antitank men, consisting of 120 men, in the Camp were 4000 Hungarians, 400 German guards and 200 S.S. and they all behaved like sheep to the British.

He found that Kramer had stayed in the Camp, why he could not imagine, and acting on Orders from Berlin had burnt all the records 2 days before.

That evening there was a riot over a potato-dump. Some German guards fired at internees who were trying to get hold of some of the potatoes. Several internees were killed.

Glynn - Hughes told Kramer that there was to be no more shooting or he would have 1 S.S. guard shot for every Internee who was shot - there was no more shooting from the Germans.

Throughout the night, high rifle fire was used to control the crowd - this did not have much effect against some Russians but one burst of machine gun fire "Hair High" stopped them.

The next morning he decided that a display of British force was indicated so he toured the Camp in a jeep, followed by tanks, armoured cars, and motor-cyclists - the people in the Camp hardly bothered to look up as the Cavalcade passed. What struck him most forcibly was the fact that neither Kramer nor the German doctor who was responsible for the health in the Camp were in the least bit ashamed about the Camp.

He made both Kramer and the doctor bury bodies but all the time they maintained an air of dumb insolence. The S.S. guards were made to bury the bodies at the double.

There was Typhus raging in Camp I. Inside the huts the conditions were appalling - the dead and the living were lying together in the huts - he personally counted 20 women living in an area of 30 square feet; a soldier, never under any conditions gets less than 45 square feet living space. There were piles of dead everywhere out in the open - these were the results of a fortnight owing to the fact that the Crematorium had broken down. Women were leaning up against these piles of dead eating their food.

The first page of Michael Hargrave's original handwritten diary. The typewritten copy printed in this book was later typed out by Michael's secretary.

95 MEDICAL STUDENTS TO HELP AT BELSEN

Evening Standard Reporter

Ninety-five volunteer medical students from London hospitals leave to-night for the notorious concentration camp at Belsen to assist the medical authorities there in the treatment of the starving, liberated men.

The students, who are in the final stages of their studies, come from University College, Guy's, Bart's, St. Thomas's, London, Middlesex, King's College, St. Mary's and Westminster Hospitals.

For a month

They will travel under the auspices of the British Red Cross and St. John War Organisation, and at Belsen will work under the Civil Affairs Department of the 21st Army Group.

"The students," said a Red Cross official to me to-day, "will remain at Belsen for a month.

"They will wear the khaki battle dress bearing the double red and white flash of the Red Cross and St. John organisation, in which they have been enrolled for the visit.

"All the students answered an appeal for help at Belsen made to the medical schools

"At Belsen they will carry out their duties under the direction of experts of the Ministries of Health and Food.

"They will be split up into teams of 12—each in charge of senior student. They travel under the command of a liaison officer Mr. De Gress.

Michael Hargrave collected newspaper clippings for his diary upon return from Bergen-Belsen. Copyright Evening Standard/Independent.

MEDICAL STUDENTS OFF TO BELSEN

Ninety-five senior medical students, drawn from the London Hospital, University College, Guy's, St. Thomas's, St. Bartholomew's, St. Mary's, Westminster, and King's College, are to help in the treatment of cases of advanced starvation at Belsen camp.

The students have already left London. They will work under the direction of the Civil Affairs Branch of 21st Army Group

ARE FLYING TO BELSEN

"Evening News" Reporter

ONE HUNDRED medical students from nine London hospitals are now on their way by air to Belsen, the German concentration camp, to render aid to the sick and starving prisoners whom the Germans left there.

When volunteers were called for there was such a ready response that the list could have been filled several times over.

Selection was finally made by taking into consideration the state of the students' studies and the proximity of final examinations.

These men, who will work at Belsen for as long as they are needed, will come under the jurisdiction of the Civil Affairs Division of the British Red Cross, and will wear battledress with the double shoulder flash of the Red Cross and St. John, with the word "British" above it.

Among the party was Captain T. Crisp, M.C., who became a medical student after being invalided from the Eighth Army, in which he served in North Africa, winning the M.C.

Leader of the relief party is grey-haired last-war veteran Mr. G. De Greeff, manufacturing chemist, who has been with the British Red Cross Society in France since D-plus 23.

His will be the administration task of looking after the 100 students at Belsen.

The medical brain behind the scheme is Professor Hemmley, of University College. Although very ill he worked out a course of treatment for the starving men of Belsen which the students studied before going.

The medical students from Westminster Hospital before leaving for Belsen. Michael Hargrave is shaking hands with G.H. McNab, the Dean of Westminster Hospital Medical School. Photograph by Reg Speller/Fox Photos/Hulton Archive/Getty Images.

Westminster Hospital Medical School students 'in battledress'. Photo credit Fox Photos Ltd. The copyright owner of this photograph was not found although every effort was made to trace them and obtain permission.

Group photograph of the British medical students from London medical schools who participated in relief work at Bergen-Belsen. Brigadier H.L. Glen Hughes, Director of Medical Services 2nd Army, is seated centre. Michael Hargrave is in the second row, ninth from the right. ©Imperial War Museum (HU59497).

A general view of the squalor and filth in the camp at the point of its liberation by the British Army. ©Imperial War Museum (BU 3764).

Women needing care in the hospital huts after the occupation of the Bergen-Belsen camp. (Photograph by Mondadori Portfolio via Getty Images).

Doctors and nurses faced the foulness

Report to Britain on Belsen

It has been established beyond doubt that German doctors in Belsen horror camp injected inmates with a solution of benzol and creosote to induce paralysis, as an excuse to send their victims to the crematorium.

When our own doctors and nurses now aproach the patients with life-saving injections they cry out in terror, and beg not to be taken to the crematorium.

So writes Dr. W. R. F. Collis, a physician now working in the camp, in a preliminary report on Belsen to the British Medical Journal.

The work carried out by medical units under the direction of Lieut.-colonel J. A. D. Johnston, R.A.M.C., has produced results which have had to be seen to be believed, says Dr. Collis.

'Human laundry'

In Camp 1, 40,000 people had been confined to their huts on pain of being shot. All these people had to be cleaned and disinfected in a "human laundry."

The British Red Cross contingent, who arrived about a week after the camp was uncovered, were "immediately thrown into the fray, doing anything and everything that they were asked."

"The women, under the leadership of Sisters Silver-Jones and Beardwell, were sent into the hospital area to take care of the first 600 patients admitted, most of whom were in a dying condition.'

All honour

Of the work of the British medical students, who took over the major task of feeding and caring for the internees in the horror camp, Dr. Collis says:

"These medical students have done a work of epic gallantry, and are worthy of all honour. The stench and the foulness which these young men have endured is quite impossible to describe.

"You could smell the camp," he says, "miles away."

Dr. Collis appeals for the homeless orphans in the camp.

"The children's blocks are now the happiest in the camp. The children do not show the terror symptoms which are, perhaps, the most terrible aspect of the adult patients' mental state.

"But most have no homes to go to, no parents, no ordinary future.

"Surely somewhere in the world are people who will come forward and care for these children.

"The problem of what to do with the forsaken, almost lost, adults is immense, but one which if not tackled will make all our efforts here a waste of time."

The only crematoria oven in the Bergen-Belsen camp, 15 April 1945. Photograph by
Galerie Bilderwelt/Getty Images.

Scene inside the cleansing station, nicknamed the 'Human Laundry', which was housed in a former stable for cavalry horses at the newly established hospital for Belsen inmates. The photograph shows some of the 60 tables, each staffed by two German doctors and two German nurses, at which the sick were washed and deloused. ©Imperial War Museum (BU 5474).

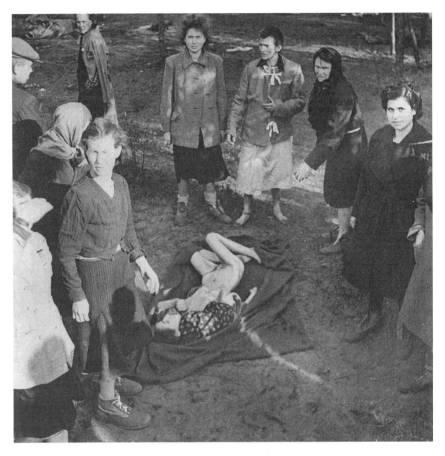

Women burying an inmate who was starved to death in the concentration camp. Photograph by LAPI/Roger Viollet/Getty Images.

A German SS guard carrying an emaciated corpse over his shoulder to one of the mass graves at Bergen-Belsen. ©Imperial War Museum (BU 4191).

German soldiers forced to load trucks with the dead bodies of the thousands of victims of the camp for burial. AP Press/Press Association.

Women carrying bodies of prisoners to a communal grave. The hut in the background is Hut 210, which Michael Hargrave was in charge of at the beginning of his month-long stay at Bergen-Belsen. AP/Press Association.

SS guard women moving bodies of their victims from a truck into a communal grave under surveillance of the Allies soldiers. Photograph by LAPI/Roger Viollet/Getty Images.

A crowd watching the burning of the last hut. Colonel Bird, Commandant of Bergen-Belsen, gave the order for the last hut at Belsen to be burnt on 21 May 1945. A rifle salute in honour of the dead was fired at the same time as a flame-thrower set fire to the last hut. A German flag and portrait of Hitler went up in flames with the hut. AP/Press Association.

Board at the entrance of the burnt Bergen-Belsen camp to remind of the horrors perpetrated at the camp. Photograph by Keystone-France/Gamma-Keystone via Getty Images.

Typhus.—Twenty-one cases have been diagnosed in this country. Fourteen were prisoners of war repatriated from Germany, and seven were medical students who were among the 100 volunteers for special duty in the Belsen concentration camp. No secondary cases had occurred since their isolation.

MEDICAL STUDENTS
Montgomery's Tribute

Field-Marshal Montgomery wrote to the Minister yesterday, expressing gratitude for the work of the students, saying:

"The work of the hundred medical students from London hospitals, originally recruited for Holland and flown out to Belsen, has been so outstanding that I must write you this personal letter of gratitude.

"What was so gratifying was the great sense of responsibility and high discipline that they showed. Perhaps it was inter-hospital rivalry, or just a natural esprit de corps, but the result was so good and the effect on their fellow-workers so great that they may all be proud of their work during this month.

"To the deans of the London hospitals I wish to express our gratitude and my assurance that these boys have not lost but rather gained in depth of experience and knowledge of humanity." (Cheers.)

There were about 10,000 dead lying around in the open and the Tommies killed about 1000 more by giving them chocolates and their own rations - 17,000 people died during March. Since we have had the Camp 13,000 people had died.

There was no Typhus in Camp II Concentration Camp and the inhabitants were fairly fit - the first scheme was to turn out all the people from Camp II and billet them out and then to evacuate Camp I into Camp II - at least the healthy people. This was not done on account of the difficulty of finding billets for the Camp II inmates. So the present scheme was put into operation and was working fairly well. Finally he thanked us all for coming out. He said that the death rate in Camp I had fallen from 500 to about 90-100 per day.

We asked him questions about the Camp and he said much the same as we were finding out for ourselves, that there was hard work with occasional beatings - but no actual atrocities, bar some cremating before the people were actually dead. Most of the atrocities were at Auschwitz.

And so to bed. Ronnie Citrine rolled in tight after playing the piano at a party the Officers were giving to the men as a victory party - they had plugged him with wine on an empty stomach!

SATURDAY May 12th.

Ralph's birthday. Up early and shaved in cold water. No diarrhoea - ½ gr. opium stopped that alright.

Found out last night that Crisp was going to start converting 217 into a Hospital. Asked George Woodward if he would like to join me in 217 as 216 was now cleared, he said he would.

Went to the Camp - got D.D.Td - collected 3 Hungies and set them to clearing everything out of the hut. Told the people in 217 - there were only 6 of them - that we were going to begin turning it into a Hospital. They all seemed quite pleased and willingly lent a hand,

Decided that I would make the 2 nurses rooms into 1 big room.   This was
easily done as the partition was only made up of wardrobes put together.

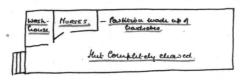

Then got the hut completely brushed out.   George then appeared and we
went off in search of a fire hose - got one from 220 but found that it would
only reach as far as the door, so we went off to try and scrounge two more
lengths.   We saw some piles of hose lying by a resevoir into which a German
fireman was pumping water, we waited until his back was turned and there was
no-one in sight and then we sneaked up and took two old lengths of hose.
Then just as we were walking off we heard a shout of "Nien! Nien!" behind us
and the German fireman dashed up, took our two lengths of old hose, went into
a hut and then came out with two brand new lengths, presented them to us
with a bow and said "these are better"!

We got the hose all fixed up, ready to start hosing the hut down after
lunch.

After lunch I hosed the hut down completely and got it quite clean as the
hose was very powerful, also got very wet myself.

The Hungies did not turn up and I was too busy to go and fetch them, so
I started to sweep the water up with Zosia helping me.

George turned up, after doing the dispensary, and started to organize the
Hungarians who were supposed to be making beds.

Crisp then turned up and got us some Hungy labour.   I then supervised the
making of the beds - boiling hot day, flies just beginning to come out, and the
Hungies did not feel like working but kept them at it, while George hosed down
the floor of the hut.

We got the whole place cleaned up and then 'cresoled' all the walls and the floor - burnt the skin off my (R) hand as I did not realize until too late what a powerful solution of cresol I had made up.

We got about 20 beds made and by keeping our Hungarians working over-time managed to get all the beds into the Hut, including 10 beds for the Nurses. We were told that we were going to get 4 more nurses. The German engineer came in and turned on the water supply to the hut.

George and I came back fit to drop. Had supper with rum and beer. Crisp says that we must be ready to-morrow as he is going to start moving patients in to-morrow afternoon, but as yet we have got no blankets or palliases.

Obviously a hard day's work ahead of me to-morrow and so am turning in early to-night.

SUNDAY May 13th.

Up at 7.15 a.m. - had breakfast, no conference and so I got to the Camp early - to find that there was some mix-up about the Hungarians and that there was no labour available. Waited for half-an-hour and managed to grab 2 Hungies. Went to 217 and collected a bed from 220 on the way.

'Organized' the 10 Hungies down there onto making beds and also the slats for them. We were very short of these later and needed about 500 by

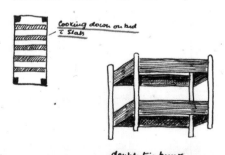

looking down on bed
2 slats

double tier bunk.

the afternoon. Then arranged the beds in the hut so that they were 3 feet apart and there were no beds opposite the windows - worked out like this we had room for 35 beds, that is 70 patients.

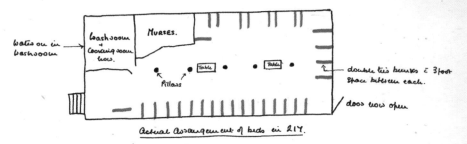

Actual arrangement of beds in 214.

The making of beds and slats went on well and soon we had the hut completely equipped with beds, though as not all the beds had slats we stopped the Hungies turning out beds and transferred them to making and cresoling slats

I managed to get the door at the far end of the hut open - the day was boiling hot and like this we got quite a good breeze going throughout the hut.

Our next headache was palliases - we got the covers from the "quartermaster" and also some straw and set our Hungies to work on filling palliases.   Got about 10 palliases filled by lunch time and $\frac{3}{4}$ of the beds now had slats.

After lunch carried on with making slats and getting the palliases filled. Got blankets from the Q.M. and Zosia and co started to make up the beds - they worked hard and well all through the day.

The ambulances came up with the patients who had been taken mainly from Hut 208 - gone through the Human Laundry at Camp I, been D.D.Td and had then come down to us.

We sprayed them and the beds with D.D.T. and then put them to bed and did any urgent dressings.   Some of the patients were in a v ery bad condition, but they were all very grateful and thankful to be on beds with palliases and blankets instead of lying in all the filth on the floor of 208.   There was a bit of difficulty because in many cases sisters had been separated as they went through the "Laundry" but we were all too busy to worry about that and hoped that it would come right in the end.

Altogether we admitted about 20 patients to-day and then the "Laundry" packed up, so George and I went off to the Q.M. stores to collect cups, plates, knives, forks, spoons, bedpans etc. and also to try and scrounge some more palliases as the supply had run out.

Collected 80 cups, 60 plates, spoons, knives and forks and 8 bedpans - more stuff to come but as the Hungies had gone we decided that the rest could wait until the morning.

Zosia, Rosa and Co invited us to tea - some butter had come from the cookhouses and they were very pleased as it was the first butter they had had for 3 years - the tea which was lukewarm was made of Grade III water - So what! We were very thirsty.

Back for supper and had 4 tots of rum, we were told that L1 and L2 were needed for the internees and so we would either have to go under canvas or double up in 14 - put my name down for canvas - should be quite nice if the weather stays fine - proposed camping site is in a field by the Mess. Went for a walk round the lake and so to bed.

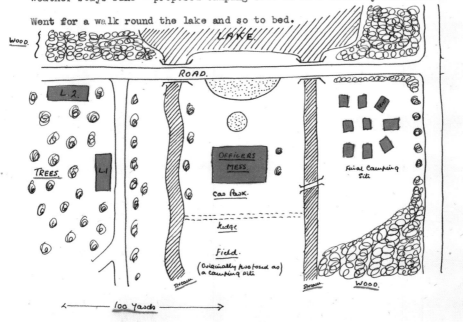

MONDAY May 14th.

Up at 7.30 - breakfast and then went to Camp I.   Not nearly so warm
to-day.

Another mess-up over the Hungarian labour - this time due to
Captain Gluck (R.A.M.C. Captain in charge of the medical part of Camp I).
After half- an - hour's wrangling managed to get hold of 2 Hungarians.

Went to 217 and much to my relief no dreadful crisis had arisen during
the night.   Perhaps it was just as well that we only had 20 patients as it
"broke in" the Nurses without too much strain.

Set 2 Hungarians making steps for the far door, as the original ones
had been used for firewood.   Set 1 Hungy to sweeping the floor and the other
to cresoling stools.

George then arrived and so did the first patients, one of us supervised
the D.D.Ting of them and getting them into bed; Zosia and co worked marvels
in the speed at which they got them into bed.

In order to cut down the work for the Nurses, George and I decided that
something had to be done about the diarrhoea so we went round giving out
Tanalbin - 5tablets stat. and then 3 tablets, 2 hourly - how we blessed my
English lessons as we tried to explain all this to Zosia.

We got all but nine beds filled by lunch time.   Lost my pentorch by
dressing an axillary ulcer while she was still on the stretcher and then
leaving my torch on the stretcher.   Probably swiped by one of the Hungy
stretcher bearers.

After lunch the other 9 patients arrived, including 1 dead woman,
probably she died of shock as she went through the "Laundry" - always surprises
me that more of them do not die, as they go through the "Laundry".

We had now got our full quota of 70 patients well spaced in a hut that once held 460 people under us and 900 under the Germans!

We now went round and had a look at the patients - they all looked much thinner now that they were clean, but in some cases they looked more healthy.

We then had to sit down and think out some system on which we were going to run our Hospital. We decided that we would have 2 sheets for each patient one at the foot of the bed with their name, age, c/o and treatment, and then another on which we would record the results of our examination.

At the end of 3 hours we had examined and written up 6 patients between us, and so some revision of the scheme was needed. Decided that the first thing to be done was to find those people who had hunger Oedema and get Casein Hydrolyzate into them.

Went round and found that we had over 40 cases of quite bad Oedema and that 18 of these were urgent.

There was one Italian girl, aged 18 - very weak, post Typhus weakness unable to walk or eat and who would certainly die if something was not done quickly. Tried to pass some of the tubing which we had to use as stomach tubes via the nasal route - could not get it down as it kinked (afterwards found that David Bowler had the same trouble) and so I passed it orally and much to my surprise it slipped down quite easily (the only lubricant we had was tea!) - then set up a protein Hydrolyzate drip GAVAGE!!!, ran in one bottle of Hydrolyzate in $\frac{1}{2}$ an hour, and then started another bottle going at about 40 drops to the minute.

George then had a go at passing a stomach tube on another girl with Oedema - she did not like it and vomited hard, so we gave up the attempt on her.

Had tea with Zosia and Co, quite enjoyed it and then we drove back to Camp II in a car which George had managed to wangle off an R.A.F. Padre, who brought round 3 R.A.F. cars to hand over to the O.C. Belsen Camp, but George managed to convince him that he did not want to give them to the O.C. Belsen Camp but to the relief workers i.e. the Medical Students and then 3 of them grabbed the cars and drove off before he could find out his mistake, George grabbing one and driving a car for the first time in his life.

Our washing came back after supper and was given out, 1 towel and several handkerchiefs were missing. Someone had gone into Dados and collected 100 watches and we were each given a watch.

Also told that we were going to move under canvas to-morrow morning.

Heard that Marlene Dietrich had been to the Camp looking for her sister and had found her there!

TUESDAY May 15th.

Got up early and started to pack up my room. Found that I had got a touch of diarrhoea again and also a spot of nausea - packed up as well as I could and then went and had breakfast - did not feel like eating much.

After breakfast transferred all my belongings including my spring bed, table and chair, to the tent which I am sharing with George Woodwark. He still had his car and we transported several of the heavier things in this.

We heard that Arthur Baines, who had had a fever and headache the day before, had gone to the German Hospital as a patient - it was thought that it might be Typhus.

George and I hitched a lift to the camp on an ambulance, as he had been found out in his car racket and he was not allowed to drive it out of Camp II.

When we reached the Camp collected 2 Hungarians and then went to 217. Here we decided that we would content ourselves with filling in the form at the foot of each bed which we had designed.

We filled in what the patients complained of and then treated them, symptomatically, writing down whatever treatment we gave and the date.

There was much diarrhoea and also some very bad cases of Oedema.

The Italian girl, to whom I gave the Casein Hydrolyzate by stomach tube, had died. She died about $\frac{2}{3}$ of the way through the second bottle of Hydrolyzate - we were rather worried in case we had passed it down the trachea, but decided that as she was able to speak to a certain

Nº of Bed	NAME	AGE
Date	Complaint	Treat-ment.
	Continuation of overleaf	

our "model" form.

extent and had no respiratory embarrassment that it had been in the stomach alright.

Most of our treatment was directed against diarrhoea - though treated one case of ? Rheumatic fever with 40 gr. Aspirin. Saw one case of quite severe Cancrum Oris - there was nothing we could do about it except give her Permanganate Mouth Washes.

After lunch - I did not feel like eating much - we carried on with our ward round which was getting a bit boring as it all had to be done through our interpreter Zosia and the going was hard.

George had managed to regain his car for the afternoon and so we took a woman who had a large abscess at the base of her (L) Index finger, to Hut 209 where there was a minor Surgery of sorts. We had to wait for

about half an hour, in order to get a vaguely sterile knife and then while
I acted as Honarary Anaesthetist and sprayed Ethyl Chloride onto it George
opened it - had a bit of difficulty as the knife was not quite so sharp as
he had expected.   We felt a bit annoyed after having waited for half an
hour to get a sterile knife, to get a blunt one given us!   Dressed it with
Gauze and Acriflavine;   Zosia had come with us and was so pleased with the
car ride that George drove her all round the Camp which pleased her immensely.

I was beginning to feel pretty rotten by this time as my Nausea was
increasing - did one more dressing and then we were invited to tea by Zosia,
could not very well refuse and so sat there while George ate hard, eating
pancakes filled with jam and I nearly vomited.

We drove back to the Camp and gave a lift to 2 Tommies;half way to the
Camp the petrol ran out, but luckily we managed to get a full can off a
passing jeep.

When we got back we found that 3 Internee women had tried to loot our
tent - they had emptied our kitbags onto the grass and were walking off with
our packs and haversacks when they were caught and driven off.

At supper we heard that Ronnie Citrine had lost all his kit except for
his greatcoat, all looted by the internees, including a gold cigarette case
worth £25, which he had brought over by mistake.

Ate 1 sardine at supper, finished rearranging the tent and went to bed
still feeling pretty rotten.

Hut 217 returns = Total = 80.

                Sick   = 70
                Nurses = 10
                dead   = 2 (1 died in afternoon).

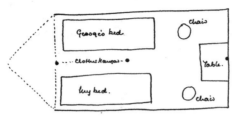

Layout of our Tent

WEDNESDAY May 16th.

Was up during the night with diarrhoea and vomiting.   Got up for
breakfast but felt so awful that I did not go to the camp - but sat outside
my tent in a chair and wished that I was back in England: constipated!

The trouble with this sort of diarrhoea is that while you have got it,
you can think of nothing else but - diarrhoea.

Camp II is now filled with internees who are turning what was once a
really beautiful camp into a cess-pit.   Went up and had a look at L2, and
it really was a heart-breaking sight, all our gas masks and tinhats which
we had had to put in one room, as they were all being recalled, had been so
smashed about as to be almost completely unrecognisable.   Saw 1 man chopping
up a cupboard for fire wood!

Anything in L2 which they could not loot they smashed, including the
wash basins and iron stoves.

At lunch I heard that 10,000 cigarettes had been looted from the
'Comforts' store in Camp I, the culprits have not been caught, but yesterday
they caught one man in the act of looting - he was taken to the Guardhouse
(after he had been D.D.Td) and was then taken to Celle where he will appear
before an allied court charged with looting.

It is rather rotten as all these cigarettes were given up by the
soldiers and R.A.F. in the district for the internees.

Did not go to the hut at all to-day and ate very little but tried to keep the fluid intake up, felt thoroughly rotten in the afternoon but fortunately I went to sleep for most of it.

In the evening went up to have a bath only to find that the water was lukewarm, which did not make me feel any better.

Came back to the tent, took 1 grain opium and some Magnesium Peroxide, and went to bed early.

£   6

THURSDAY May 17th.

Feeling just as bad to-day and did not get up for breakfast.   At about 10 o'clock Dr Meiklejohn came and saw me and said that there was not much to be done, except to wait for it to go and to keep up the fluid intake.

Got up at about 11 o'clock and sat in the sun, but it was so hot that I had to sit in the shade.

George came back at about 11.45 feeling awful and looking pretty rotten, like me, he also had the queer feeling that after he had walked about 10 yards his legs were going to give way under him and it felt just as if we had been in bed for about a month and then just got up.   Having a rest did not seem to help this terrible feeling of weakness.

George has also got a feeling of stiffness in his (L) deltoid - where he had his Typhus injections and thinks that he may be having an abortive attack of Typhus.

At lunch heard that Arthur Baines was vomiting every $\frac{1}{4}$ of an hour and that his temperature was beginning to rise, but that he was still not diagnosed.

In the afternoon George and I both went to sleep and did not wake up until about 6 o'clock.   When we woke I was feeling much better and he was about the same.

Had supper and then sat in the tent all evening. Learnt that George's father (Sir Stanley Woodwark) died 3 days ago of Coronary Thrombosis. Felt very sorry for George. I had only seen his father once, and that was at the Shrove Tuesday dinner at Westminster, but he struck me as being an extremely nice man and must have been an equally nice father. Rotten luck for George to be out in Germany when he died.

We both went to bed early - hoping to feel better to-morrow.

FRIDAY May 18th.

Had a good night and felt much better in the morning, so did George. Ate a good breakfast and then went down to Camp I.

We had been told at breakfast that all of Crisp's Hospital area in the Camp totalling some 800-900 patients was to be evacuated to-day into the "Roundhouse" in Camp II, which had been equipped with beds and was ready to become a Hospital.

When I got down to 217, found that the ambulance teams were already evacuating Hut 213 which was just next to us. The rumour went round that they were not taking patients unless they had been washed and.D.D.Td, so I set the Nurses to work washing the patients, a job they did not like at all as many of the patients had scabies. I went up to the main gate in order to get a tin of D.D.T.

On the way up I watched them burning three of the huts in the men's laager. They soaked them in petrol and oil and then set light to them - clouds of black smoke rose up and then floated out over the German country-side - luckily for us the wind was blowing away from Camp II. It took about 10 minutes for a hut to be completely destroyed.

On the way back from the main gate met George Woodwark and then together we saw Crisp and explained to him that it was quite impossible to get all the patients washed by the time they were due to leave - he agreed and said that he had never given the order that they should be washed anyway!

Went back to the hut and told the nurses that they could stop washing the patients, but that they all had to be sprayed with D.D.T. they quite enjoyed this work and so our shares rose considerably.

We then saw the American Ambulance people and found out that our hut would not be evacuated until the afternoon, so we had some time to have a look round the patients - found that several of them had died, mostly those that I had expected to die, including the Cancrum Oris, and that several other patients were in 'Status Gravis'. George and Russell Barton, who had helped in my absence, had been trying to get them to drink protein Hydrolyzate, a Herculean task as the stuff smelt just like vomit, but the results on the Oedema had not been very encouraging.

We went round giving each patient who had diarrhoea $\frac{1}{2}$gr. opium - there were less cases of diarrhoea than 3 days ago, indicating that the new dosage of Tanalbin had worked.

I was then presented with the bombshell, which George had warned me yesterday he thought was coming. Zosia and the rest of the nurses said that when the patients went to Camp IV Hospital (Roundhouse) they did not want to carry on nursing them.

Personally I do not blame them at all as no compensation is offered to them for nursing. All the other fit internees have quite a good time with no work to do and they just wander around all day looting and agitating to go back to their countries - while the nurses have to work hard and because they are doing good work will probably be the last people to go back to their countries.

The only difficulty was that they thought that as soon as they got into Camp IV it would only be a matter of days before they were repatriated to Poland.

Tried to explain to them why they would not be going back to Poland for many months as there were neither houses nor food nor Government in Poland at the moment.   Then I had to sit down and explain the International situation about Poland to them; all about the Curzon Line and the 'Lublin Poles' etc, they all wanted the London Government and would rather die than live on the wrong side of the Curzon Line as they hate the Russians just as much as the Germans, saying that they got no better treatment at the hands of the Russians when they marched into Poland in 1939 than they did at the hands of the Germans.   They said all this after being in German Concentratin Camps for 3 years.

After they had explained all this to me (they all lived on the wrong áide of the Curzon Line) with many gesticulations and flashing eyes, I had an uncomfortable feeling that they held me responsible for the International situation and so, deeming that discretion was the better part of valour, I beat a hasty retreat for lunch.

At lunch George and I decided that I should go down to the Hut in order to supervise the evacuation and that he would go up to the Roundhouse to meet the patients on their arrival there.

So went down to the Hut and learnt that the ambulances would be coming to 217 in about half an hour.   So I went and had a look at what I thought was one of the most impressive things about the Camp.

It was a pile of boots, made up of the boots taken off the victims they cremated.   I don't know how many years it had taken the Germans to build up this pile, but it was about 20 yards long by about 5 yards across and about 12 feet high - the shoes at the bottom were squashed as flat as paper and so you can imagine how many thousands of pairs of shoes there were there, and each pair of shoes had once had an owner, and though the Germans may have destroyed all the records of the Camp, this pile of shoes and boots bore mute but absolutely damning evidence of the number of people who had died in this Camp before the British arrived, because we did not add the shoes of the dead onto this pile, and yet we buried 23,000 people.

The ambulances then arrived and such was the speed at which they were working that they cleared the whole hut in 10 minutes.

There was one woman, whom I did not evacuate, she was aged 18, she was Comatose and obviously dying fast and when I examined her I found that she had absolutely classical Cheyne Stokes Respiration

On account of the fact that she was obviously going to die it seemed a waste of time to take her to the "Roundhouse".

My next headache was getting the nurses packed up and into the lorry which was waiting to take them to Camp IV, found that once the patients had gone they had all gone off for a walk except Zosia so I told her to start packing and went off in the lorry to find the others.   Found them and took them back to the hut - in all it took me about 2 hours to get 10 nurses packed up, but eventually all was ready and so leaving a notice nailed to the door saying that there was one dying and Comatose woman in the hut, we drove off saying good-bye to Hut 217 for the last time.

Was not quite sure what I was going to do with Zosia and Co but they were on my hands now and I had to find them somewhere to sleep for the night.

Drove up to the "Roundhouse" and saw Mrs Crossthwaite and she told me to take them to the office in Camp II. Took them there and they told me that I would have to take them to the office in Camp III - when I got there they said that before they could take them they would have to be registered. Just as I was taking them off to be registered, the Army Major who was in charge of Camp III said that they had stopped admitting people for the day and that I would have to take them to 612 Military Government in Camp II - we went there and in the office I found a Major and a Captain, the Major told the Captain that they could not take them and that they must go to Camp IV - the Major then left to go riding and the Captain said it was O.K. and he would fix them up for the night in Camp II and then see that they were transferred to Camp IV in the morning.

So we drove round to one of the German stables which had been equipped with beds and palliases and got them fixed up for the night. Then I said good-bye to them and thanked them for all the help they had given me, and drove off back to the Mess to arrive just in time for supper.

I hope Zosia and Co get comfortable billets in Camp IV as they have worked hard and are probably stuck here for many months and possibly for the whole of the winter.

After supper I went up to the Roundhouse to have a look round - found that they had converted the Banquet - cum - dance hall into a ward and that it con- tained about 200 beds and that all the rooms off the two flanking passages which used to be the German Officers rooms had been converted into wards.   The two large semicircular rooms jutting out at the back of the buildings, because they had such large windows and were so light, had been made into T.B. Sanatoria.

Managed to locate most of the patients from 217 in wards 1 and 12 - they were all very hungry but were on spring beds with palliases and blankets.

They had been given brown bread and margarine and they wanted the biscuits which they had been having in the hut - still nothing has been done about getting them white bread and giving them brown bread is just a complete waste of time as they will not eat it.

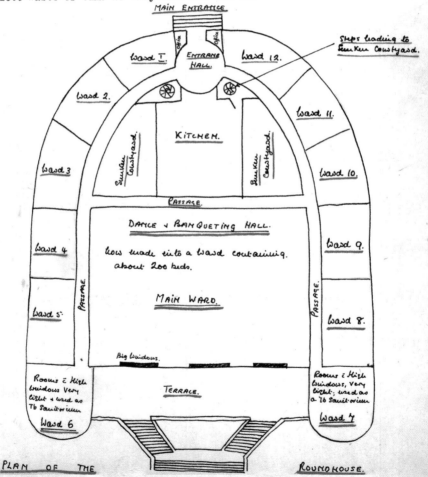

PLAN   OF   THE   ROUNDHOUSE.

Someone had liberated about 100 fountain pens from Dados and we drew lots for them. I got a 'Waterman' which will probably write with a bit of coaxing, if I can get hold of some ink for it, which is scarce in these parts

---

SATURDAY May 19th.

Cold this morning but the sun was up - felt hearty and so had a share out in the open - only just arrived in time for breakfast.

After breakfast George and I went up to the Roundhouse (only about 400 yards away from the mess) - gone are the days of having to 'hitch' transport to Camp I.

We were allotted wards 1 and 12 and in those we located about half our patients, the rest had gone into other wards in the chaos of yesterday. Our patients all seemed quite pleased to see us - mainly I think because they thought that we were going to give them food.

We started to do a ward-round of all our patients (totalling now 42), acting in the same way as we had done in our own Hospital - giving only palliative treatment but keeping the usual record at the end of the bed of what they complained of and what treatment was given.

An R.A.M.C. Captain from the Army Blood Transfusion Unit came round and we pointed out our worst cases of Oedema and working on the principle that the cause of the Oedema was loss of plasma proteins due to malnutrition they started to transfuse 3 of them with reconstituted double strength plasma. There was one girl with diarrhoea with blood in her stools (? dysentery) and on account of her gross anaemia we started to transfuse her with whole blood. This took most of the morning - before we left for lunch we had managed to get one bottle a-piece into the 3 people we were transfusing with plasma.

Came back after lunch and found that 2 of the people being transfused with plasma were tolerating it well, but that the third was restless.   By slowing the drip down to one drop every 7 seconds she quietened down and took the remainder of the second bottle well.

In the case of the whole blood transfusion, we had great difficulty in keeping the drip going - did not think that we were properly in a vein and so I took the needle out and tried again - after that it went alright. Gave $\frac{1}{2}$ grain of phenobarbitone to those being transfused and it kept them quiet very nicely.

Carried on with the ward round doing any dressings which were needed, then went round and had a look at the 3 Oedemas which were having plasma.

The plasma was not having the miraculous effect upon the Oedema which I had hoped that it would have, but perhaps it is too early yet.

The transfusion people were going to give them each a third bottle but persuaded them not to as all 3 of them had had Typhus and complained of weak hearts and I was frightened that 3 pints would overload the heart.

Oval glucose-Vitamin solution was then brought round to ward 12 while I was not there, and one of the 'Nurses' began pouring it down the throat of a semi-comatose patient, who promptly aspirated it.   'Nurse' dashed into Ward 1 where I was and tried to explain what had happened.   When I got there she was breathing with difficulty and her breathing was very laboured and bubbling - definitely Cyanosed.   Listened to her chest and heard nothing except bubbling vales right up to the Apices - there was nothing except I could do for her except sit her up and hope that all the fluid would collect at the bases of her lungs and that any broncho pneumonia would be localized to the lower lobes, but she was too full of fluid and died about 10-15 minutes later.   Felt extremely annoyed with the nurse, with the R.A.M.C.

orderly for leaving the Glucose with an untrained nurse, and with myself for not being there, because it was an easily avoidable death and with so many people dying anyway we do not want any avoidable deaths.

Came back to mess and had dinner. After that we were each given our N.A.A.F.I. bottle of whisky (price 8/6) and the Panzer trousers to match our coats, then had a bath and went to bed.

Found out that one of the nurses in Ward I was a Sulphathiazole addict and so promptly removed all the tablets of Sulphathiazole from that ward - don't think that I will be very popular with her to-morrow.

SUNDAY May 20th.

Up at 8 o'clock - we had marmalade for breakfast but not much; went up to the Roundhouse and George and I started on our usual morning ward round.

Hunted out the cases which had been transfused and found that the double strength plasma had considerably reduced the Oedema but had not completely got rid of it, but that it had not done much good as far as the general condition of the patient was concerned.

We marked out more cases to be transfused with plasma but the transfusion people were keen to try out the 5% Casein Hydrolyzate which they had got with them and so we set up two drips going as a clinical trial. They took the Hydrolyzate much better than the plasma and we gave them two bottles each at the rate of about 1 drop per second - by the time we left it had not had much effect upon the Oedema and as no glucose was given at the same time I do not expect much result from it as they will just burn up the Hydrolyzate as fuel.

As for the rest of the patients, they all seem to be picking up quite quickly, and are all eager for cigarettes. They are still a little scared about taking fresh milk and other fluids while they have diarrhoea - a

"Belsen Fallacy" which has probably killed as many people as the actual

famine.

Saw one woman who had some very large caseating glands tuberculous

glands in the neck, with a long track under the jaw to an external opening

just beneath the chin - could only treat

it with dry dressings.

There is another woman who is also

a bit of a problem.   She has about 5 huge

bedsores about the size of saucers, they are all

in a filthy condition owing to the fact that she

is incontinent of faeces, one of them has become a deep sloughing ulcer which

has ulcerated right through Gluteus Maximus and now has its base formed by

the Ischial Tuberosity.   Gave her $\frac{1}{4}$ Morphine and then dressed her wound

with Sulphathizole cream and she has also the beginnings of a Cancrum Oris.

There is another woman who I suspect has got Typhus as she has the

typically suffused look with a high fever and quite bad dehydration with

headache.   Gave her 15 grains Aspirin and told the nurse to see that she

drinks a lot of water.

Have 3 other cases of fever which are a complete mystery to me.

In the afternoon carried on with the symptomatic treatment.   George

had to go off and look after the dispensary - after I had finished my ward

round went downstairs and visited George in the dispensary.   He has now

got a huge and wonderful collection of German drugs - all in Ampoules -

some difference to the miniature dispensary he had in Camp I.

Found a fire screen down there composed of 12 tiles, which I must see if I can manage to get home.

Knocked off at about 6 o'clock and then went and sat in the sun outside my tent for an hour - supper at seven, after supper wrote a letter to Daddy, then went down to the mess to have some whisky and corned beef and so to bed.

Returns from Wards 1 and 12.

Ward 12	Total = 22		Ward 1.	Total = 20
	V. Sick 11			V. Sick = 10
	No. to be evacuated = 0			No. to be evacuated = 0
	Dead = 1.			Dead = 0

MONDAY May 21st.

Up at 8 o'clock - found that there was no marmalade for breakfast - great disappointment . Went up to the round House all the patients were looking much better, more cheerful, much more interested in what was going on around them - and they were all beginning to grumble about the food etc. which is quite a good sign I think.

Had a look at the two cases which had been given the 5% I.V. Casein Hydrolyzate, in neither case had it had any effect upon the Oedema, though in both cases it had made them stronger and more interested in things, and in one case the diarrhoea had gone, but as she had also had Mist Opic and Kaolin, difficult to know which one got rid of the diarrhoea.

There was another interesting case in Ward 12, young girl aged about 19 with unilateral Oedema of her right leg from the foot up to and including the right Labium Majus she had a history of sudden onset with pain in the R.I.F. and the Oedema is now subsiding gradually. Made our diagnosis of ? External Iliac Vein Thrombosis.

Another woman who had multiple small, superficial abscesses all over her body, ? Avitaminosis and so dosed her with Army Compound Vitamin tablets

In Ward 1 there was a girl with multiple deep discharging ulcers down the inner side of her left leg, with massive Oedema of the foot. We were not sure what this was, so we showed it to Major Walker, the Army surgical specialist, who was coming round in the capacity of a Consulting Surgeon, he diagnosed it as a case of suppurative phlebitis and advised raising her leg and flavine dressings - dressed the leg and raised it on a box padded with curtains - girl was only 15 so I gave her 15g. Aspirin and ½gr. Phenobarbitone to send her to sleep.

Also decided to raise the foot of the girl with unilateral Oedema and did so with another box.

My diagnosis of the caseating glands was confirmed despite a rival suggestion that it might be Actinomycosis.

When I had finished doing dressings and dishing out tablets for diarrhoea, pain, headache etc. I went down to the dispensary and "liberated" my fire screen.

After lunch I rewrote several of the case sheets at the ends of the beds and gave out any tablets which were needed. We did not have any drips going to-day and I do not want any more Hydrolyzate as it is no use for the Oedema - the only thing which touches the Oedema is double strength plasma and several other people have had a 25% mortality from this - so I am rather chary about using it, nevertheless, I think that there are 2 cases which should have it.

The girl we transfused with whole blood is much better, her diarrhoea is going but she has got a bit of a fever now - don't know why. I think that she is one girl that we have quite definitely saved from dying as in the hut at one stage we had labelled her status gravis and now she is asking for chocolates and cigarettes.

The woman with the fever, which I think is Typhus, still has a roaring fever and suffused appearance but has still got no rash.

At 6 o'clock went along to Camp I to see the last hut in the Concentration Camp being burnt down.   There was a large crowd there - the hut (No. 47) was soaked in oil and in front of it was a large Nazi flag and also a flag with Hitler's face painted upon it.   Round the hut was a railing made of white tape, on the left were two flame throwing Bren carriers next to them was a Union Jack all neatly curled up, at the top of a flag pole and next to that a platform with microphone and loud speakers.

Troops marched down and formed a guard behind the platform, then a section marched infront of the platform and drew up there - they were the Guard of Honour for the people who had died in Belsen Camp.   The crowd then

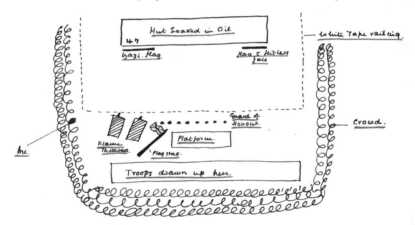

made a semi-circle round the hut and waited for whoever was going to perform the Ceremony.   While we were waiting, one of the flame-throwers accidently sent a jet of flame over the hut - some of it dropping on the hut - amidst cheers from the crowd the crew of the Bren carrier dashed towards the hut and put out the flames with fire extinguishers!

Brigadier Glynn Hughes turned up and then Colonel Bird mounted the platform and made a short but good speech - He reviewed the history of Belsen Camp since the British liberated it on April the 15th, he ended up by saying that "as the British flag did not stand for bestiality or cruelty and that was why the Union Jack had never flown over Belsen Camp - now as the last Hut was being burnt the Union Jack would fly for the first time".

Brigadier Glynn Hughes and 3 other Colonels then got into the flame-throwers and fired them aiming at the Nazi flag and Hitler and as the hut burst into flame the Union Jack floated out from the top of the flag pole. Pure ceremony and melodrama, but most impressive!

On the way back went round to have a look at the mortal remains of Hut 217 - there it was a mass of ashes - almost felt quite sorry as I had rather looked on it as home while I worked there and now it was no more, like the rest of Belsen Camp.

Looking round Belsen Camp now was like looking at a wilderness of ashes - with occasional raised squares of earth rising up out of it, each with their small piece of board saying "1000 unknown people buried here", "8000 unknown people buried here," and completely surrounding the Camp was the pine forest, which would soon grow over what remained of both Belsen Concentration Camp and the thousands of its inmates who died there.

Passed by the pile of boots, which like the rest of the Camp was a smouldering mass of ashes.

Between the administrative part of the Camp (which was still standing) and the now extinct Concentration Camp a large hoarding had been erected with the following words on it:-

This is the site of the

INFAMOUS BELSEN CONCENTRATION CAMP.

Liberated by British forces on April 15th 1945,

who when they entered found;

10,000 dead lying around on the ground
13,000 died after the liberation.

etc. etc.

Went back to Camp II, had supper and bath and then went to bed early as it had begun to rain again.

(We were photographed both by a Movie Cameraman and Dr. Meiklejohn against the background of the burning hut).

TUESDAY May 22nd.

Up at 8.15. We are steadily getting up later and later, just got down to breakfast in time to have some treacle. We are all feeling continually hungry despite the fact that we appear to get quite a lot to eat - main trouble is lack of jam etc. to go on the bread.

As it was my morning off and there was not much to do at the roundhouse I decided that I would take the morning off; lounged around and tidied up the tent a bit as it was beginning to bear a strong resemblance to the conditions in Camp I.

Then feeling bored, (it was raining and so I could not sit out in the sun) I wandered up to the Roundhouse and found George doing a round of the patients and explaining what they had got to the Polish woman doctor from Hut 210. She and another doctor were supposed to tide over the time when we left and the 29th British General Hospital arrived.

Joined in the round and started a woman on a course of Sulphathiazole (Oedema of right forearm followed an infected area on dorsum of right hand) 3 grammes stat and 1 gramme 4 hourly with fluids + +

We had found that in several cases, patients whom we treated with Sulphathiazole for some reason or other lost their diarrhoea and so as many other people also reported favourably on the use of Sulphathiazole in curing diarrhoea, we started about 5 patients who had reacted neither to Tanalbin or opium on Sulphathiazole.

Then went down to the "Dispensary" and collected a couple of cardboard cartons in order to pack up my glasses. Came back to the tent and waited anxiously for lunch.

After lunch, which consisted of Bully Beef, went up to the Roundhouse and did a "treating round" of the patients - the diarrhoea appears to be getting very much better, only about 10 people now have diarrhoea badly. The Oedema of the legs is going down now that we have elevated them - made a sloping incline with bandages wound round a wooden framework - this was more comfortable than a wooden box and she was not likely to get pressure sores on her heels.

The girl with the unilateral Oedema of the right leg is now much better, and the Oedema of the leg is going down. Set another woman, who had Anasarca, going on a double strength plasma drip - she has already had two bottles of 5% strength Casein Hydrolyzate and it did not even touch her. Casein Hydrolyzate has I think been dropped. Professor Davidson (Professor of Medicine, Edinburgh) asked us some questions about the work etc. He said that some Edinburgh students were coming out afterwards.

He raised some interesting points about the treatment of diarrhoea - basing the treatment upon whether the cause was Mechanical or Infective.

Thought it over in the evening and came to the conclusion that as regards any concentration camps which may be liberated in the far East, if someone can find a quick and reliable cure for diarrhoea there is no need for any other form of treatment, as once you have stopped the diarrhoea the patients regain both their appetite and their strength - over $\frac{3}{4}$ of the treatment which I have given at Belsen has gone towards trying to cure diarrhoea and as I have said before there must have been many hundreds of deaths at Belsen Camp solely due to the exhaustion following diarrhoea.

Methods used here:

Mechanical   (Opium - good but habit forming.
                       (Tanalbin - good in large enough doses.

Infective   (Sulphathiazole - good in cases which do not react to
                  (opium or Tanalbin

? Pellagra   (Nicotinic Acid - sometimes succeeds in cases not reacting
                (to any of the 3 preceding.

Famine   (Casein Hydrolyzate - ? some people say that it is of
                (value.

and so the cure undoubtedly depends upon whether the cause is

(1) Mechanical
(2) Infective

But it is not so easy just to look at a patient and decide whether the cause is mechanical or Infective. The only practical thing to do is to try one cure, the Mechanical first as it is easier to give opium and Tanalbin than a course of Sulphonamide, and then if it does not react to that treatment switch onto the other one.

If of course the diarrhoea is due to the rich food which they are eating after a long period of semi-starvation, you are in a bit of a quandary because you want to get the food into them and yet you MUST stop the diarrhoea.   Perhaps in these cases Oval Hydrolyzate with $\frac{1}{2}$ Gr. Opium is the answer.

———————

Went to the films in the evening "Show Business", came back and had some bully beef in the Mess and then went to bed.

———————

WEDNESDAY May 23rd.

Up at 8 o'clock to-day and had an egg for breakfast also had diarrhoea again.   After breakfast I went up to the Roundhouse, and did a round of all the patients.   Nothing very much to report except that in 4 out of 5 cases the Sulphathiazole has cured the diarrhoea.

Gave one woman an I.V. Mercurial duiretic as she has Oedema of hands feet, abdominal wall etc.   She has already had 2 bottles of Intravenous Casein Hydrolyzate - but although this appeared to make her stronger it did not help the Oedema.

Did some dressings in Ward I and decided that I would leave Ward 12 until after lunch.

At lunch we had the usual bully beef, we are all getting fed up with it as we have had it for the last 3 days.

After lunch carried on in Ward 12.   The girl with the T.B. Glands and a sinus has now got 2 openings beneath her chin, one from some caescating caescating glands on the left side of her neck now.

She also has some crepitations at the
Apices of both lungs and as she has a bad
cough she probably also has pulmonary T.B.
She is one of the cases whose diarrhoea was

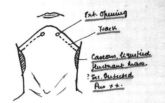

stopped by Sulphathiazole - the only disadvantage about her is that she does
not like having the nurse dress her Sinuses, and so I have to do it each
day which pleases her immensely!

Had to dress the leg of the girl with suppurative phlebitis - did not
want to do it - but the nurse flatly refused to do it as there was so much
foul smelling pus knocking around and so as there was no-one else to do it,
I had to; all her ulcers look much cleaner but they are still discharging
pus hard.   The Oedema is not going down because she will not keep her foot
up but bends her knee.   Decided to give her one more chance and so I
dressed it with flavine gauze and told her to keep her leg straight.

Crisp came and told us that Professor Davidson had decided to stay on
at Belsen for another 2 days and that he would be doing a ward round at
5 o'clock to see any cases of famine Oedema.   We told him that we had one
case and then we were told that he expected a proper case history and
continuation notes!

Fortunately we managed to get hold of an interpreter and George asked
the questions while I wrote down the answers - just as well for us that
we had the interpreter as the woman was (a) Hungarian, (b) Mad (c) could
not speak much German anyway.

Eventually we managed to get some sort of History out of her
(fortunately not one of Nephritis as she was the same woman to whom I had
given the Mercurial dieretic in the morning).   Copied out her continuation notes to learn that Davidson was not coming round to-day after
all.

Heard that we are going back to England on Saturday or within 48 hours.

Went back to have supper, it has been raining all day and we are all feeling depressed and dismal. After supper filled in some forms on disease incidence, results of treatment of diarrhoea and Oedema, and the Value of I.V. Plasma and Casein Hydrolyzate.

Had a bath - on the way up to the bathhouse met Zosia and Rosa. Zosia does not look so nice now that she has tried to make up, as she did in Camp I. She is still trying to learn English, but has no-one to teach her.

Most of the women in Camp I seem to be getting their self-respect back - now that they are in decent clothes, (every man, woman and child in the province of Luneberg in which Belsen is situated has had to give up 1 suit of clothes for the internees); they are attempting to keep themselves clean and to look nice.

Somehow I cannot bring myself to like the internees as they are making such an infernal mess of this camp, and all their destruction is so wanton as they destroy anything which is of no use to them at the present moment, irrespective of the fact that they might want it later, and they still live by the "law of the clutching hand".

And so to bed.

THURSDAY May 24th.

Only just got up in time for breakfast to-day. After breakfast George and I went up to the Roundhouse to do the usual morning ward round - gave some Santorium tablets to a woman who claimed that she had passed a worm - she also had extremely advanced tubercle.

. Noticed for the first time that nearly all the young girls (15 - 19)
who we had in our wards, were Italian. The rest were mainly Poles and
Hungarians with an occasional German Jew.

Decided that we would leave most of the dressings until after lunch as
Professor Davidson was coming this morning and was going to give a ward round.

He did turn up at 11 o'clock followed by a Brigadier, 5 Colonels and
umpteen Captains and they were given the Ward round and not us - most of our
thoughts and sayings on the matter were quite unprintable.

Carried on with our private ward round and then went off to have some
lunch. At lunch there was great excitement about the dance which we were
going to hold this evening - as far as we could gather there was going to be
no shortage of drink.

After lunch went round doing the dressings. The girl with the Supp.
phlebitis still would not keep her leg straight and so after I had dressed
her leg I made a splint and bandaged her leg down onto it which rather
shook her.

We are all beginning to feel bored with the life out here now because
we feel that our work has really been done and what is needed here now is a
competent nursing staff with about 10 doctors to go round and have a look at
the patients each day and tell the nurses what to do.

We have not got enough time to examine each patient fully and yet there
is too much time to do just symptomatic treatment - one thing is certain
however, and that is that all the patients are looking much better and are
stronger though they are still phenomenally thin.

We have no Hungarian labour inside the Hospital, instead German women
are made to come in from the surrounding towns and wash the floors etc.

Went back to my tent at about 6 o'clock in order to shave and wash

before supper, which was at 6.30.   After supper we lounged around until
7.30 when the dance was due to begin.   Actually it did not begin until
8 o'clock.

There was a distinct shortage of women, but as there was no shortage
of drink, which was what everyone had come for anyway, we did not worry.
We had:-

    Rum Punch with Benedictine.
    Gin and Lime.
    Hock.
    Chianti.
    Lemonade and a Buffet.

I went to bed about twelve o'clock but the party went on till about
3 o'clock.   Got up to the tent just in time to find George Woodwark, who
had turned in early as he was trying to hitch-hike to Berlin to-morrow,
starting to groan and so I hastily pushed a bucket towards him into which he
vomited with masterly precision.

$\frac{3}{4}$ of an hour later I was retching my guts out into the self same bucket.

Derek Wells is in the German Hospital with Typhus.

FRIDAY May 25th.

George got up at 6 o'clock this morning in his attempt to get to Berlin
and so I did not see him all day.   I got up at 8.30 and found to my surprise that I had not got a hang-over at all - Dick Jenkins on the other hand
stayed in bed all morning as he had a splitting headache.

Went up to the Roundhouse not feeling like doing any work at all.
Nevertheless did the usual ward round.

Had a look at the "cholinised" drip which Russell Barton and I had set
up yesterday afternoon containing 6 mgm of Acetyl Choline, 1 cc 1/1000
Adrenaline in 1 pint of plasm

Adrenaline in 1 pint of plasma.   It was Russell's idea, working on the principle that choline was a stimulant to Kidney function and therefore the Oedema would go down through the fluid being excreted - her Oedema was certainly less, but as it was impossible to keep any record of the Urinary Volume, we had no proof that the benefit which she had got had not come from the plasma, but as the other woman which I had got on single strength plasma was no better, there was circumstantial evidence that the choline was working.

Carried on doing the dressings - the girl whose leg I splinted has now reduced her Oedema by half - but was beginning to get a sore back as she was unable to turn over with a splint on her leg, so I got a palliass half filled with straw and put that behind her and thus got her sitting up after which she was more comfortable.

We have only got about 3 cases of diarrhoea left now and we have put these onto Nicotinic Acid 300mgm daily, as many of the others say that they have found that it cures diarrhoea.

The girl with the unilateral Oedema of her right leg is now completely better except she has got a stiff knee, but this will go as with a little coaxing she can flex and extend it all right.   In fact all the patients are very much better and need nothing so much as good nursing.

After lunch carried on with any treatment and dressings which still remained to be done.   Got these finished fairly early and went back to the tent and packed - especially my liberated wine glasses - finished both my packing and also adjusting my equipment and then three of us started throwing bayonets at trees - stuck a bayonet in my left index finger.   David Bowler sprayed it with Sulphonamide and dressed it.

There was nothing much to do in the evening after supper and so I
lounged around - heard that some Belgian medical students had arrived and
that we were going to hand over to them to-morrow. Also that the High
Commissioner for South Africa had visited the Roundhouse in the afternoon.
I had seen him but had had no idea who he was.

George had still not come back from his jaunt to Berlin and I began to
wonder if he was going to get back at all to-night as it is a good 200 miles
to Berlin.

And so to bed.

_____ _____

SATURDAY May 26th.

Woke up to find that George had got back all right at about 11 o'clock
last night and found out that he had not managed to get to Berlin as he had
been turned back by the Russians on the far side of the Elbe, but he had had
quite an enjoyable day.

Had another egg for breakfast and then George insisted that as he had
had the day off yesterday I should have it off to-day. I agreed and spent
the morning packing up some wine glasses which I had got off Russell Barton
and lounging around waiting for lunch - there was nothing else to do as it
was raining again to-day.

After lunch I decided that rather than be bored for the rest of the
afternoon I would go up to the Roundhouse and so I went round with George
Woodwark - the Nicotinic Acid seemed to be clearing up the remaining
diarrhoeas quite nicely and we now had only 1 case of really bad diarrhoea.
We did some dressings - about the only treatment which was now needed.

We were told that we were going to hand over to the Belgian medical students at 4.30. Meanwhile some Army Nursing Sisters and a Major from the 29th British General Hospital had arrived and there were several blow-ups between the nursing sisters and our chaps - the sisters tried to order them around in their own wards and as we were still in charge they were told, none too politely, where they got off.

Then the Matron went round and started to critize our Hospital and another chap blew up at her. It was a great pity that these people had not seen the conditions in Camp I and been able to compare them with the Round-house!

Tempers were beginning to run pretty high when the Belgian students arrived - I showed two of them round our wards and explained what each patient had got and when I had finished one of the students asked me where the tem-perature charts were - I had to carefully explain to them that we did not even have thermometers, which rather shook them!

We then said good-bye to Mrs Crossthwaite and we had handed over the Roundhouse. Our work at Belsen had now come to an end and in many ways we were not sorry. The Light Ack-Ack had left a couple of days ago, going off at about 8 o'clock in the morning with no-one to send them off. We had not realized that they were going until they had gone when it was too late. It was a great pity because they had done an immense amount of work for the camp and had been the original people into it.

I In the evening went up to see a show at the cinema called the "Barn Stormers". George and I took a little internee boy in and he promptly went to sleep on my lap. Left half way through the show in order to listen to a talk given by Captain Davis of the American Typhus Commission. He demonstrated a case of Typhus and then gave us a talk on how they had controlled the Typhus Epidemic at Belsen.

He was extremely good and I took notes on the back of some German Propaganda postcards.

We should have been going home to-day but learnt that the transport had only been applied for, for Monday.   And so to bed.

SUNDAY May 27th.

Got up so late this morning that both George and I missed breakfast. Managed to scrounge some bread and jam and ate that.

After breakfast went up to the Bath-house and had a bath and a shave - found that the water was almost cold and that did not improve our already frayed tempers.   I sat out in the sun for the rest of the morning while George did some packing.

After lunch we heard that Dr. Meiklejohn was going into Celle to arrange for Hospital accommodation and was willing to take 4 of us in with him, so George Woodwark, Dick Jenkins and David Bowler and myself decided to go with him.   Lionel Garstin, Meiklejohn's driver, drove us in.

The road was extremely bad all the way and we looked with interest at the German countryside and civilians.   One thing struck me forcibly, and that was that all the Germans were laughing and happy, except when they saw our truck and that soon wiped the smile off their faces.

Another thing was that all the German women and children were fair haired and that a dark head was the exception - in Belsen I do not remember seeing a blonde the whole time I was there.

We drove into Celle, which is an extremely pretty town, and then up to

the Hospital which had been used under the Germans for poison gas experi-
ments - here Meiklejohn disappeared into the office and we sat and waited for
him.   After an hour he said that the man he was looking for was at a foot-
ball match and that we had better drive round while we waited for him.

So we drove into Celle, found an R.A.F. information Centre and asked
them if there was anywhere where we could get tea in Celle - they said no,
and our opinion of both Celle and the R.A.F. dropped with a bang.

Went for a drive along the Brunswick road and then drove back to the
Hospital to pick up Meiklejohn; on the way back to Celle noticed that all
the German houses were different from one another and that they do not have
the rows upon rows of houses, all exactly the same, like we do.

When we got back to the Camp found that Russell Barton had made a raft
out of Duck boards and four beer barrels and was happily punting himself
round the lake.

Nothing much to do in the evening except wonder whether we would be
going home to-morrow - bet George that we would and we had a bob on it.

Went to the Cinema and saw "Flesh and Fantasy".   Good film but I had
seen it before - came back to the mess to find an ambulance drawn up outside
the Mess and found that another of our chaps was being taken off with Typhus
- rotten luck when we are due to go home so soon.

We heard also that the Belgian students were completely lost up at the
Roundhouse - standing round in groups, not knowing what to do.

————————— ——————

Had several group photographs taken to-day.   One of the Westminster
group and one of the "Roundhouse" group standing on the front steps of the
Roundhouse with Brigadier Glynn Hughes.

MONDAY May 28th.

Made sure that we got up in time for breakfast this morning and had 2 eggs for breakfast - these were got by Dick Jenkins and Ken Easton who used to go out to the local German farmhouses and give 1 cigarette for 2 eggs - highly illegal as barter is strictly forbidden out here.

Looked as though it was going to be a fine day and so I sat around in the sun for the first part of the morning. No message had come through to say that we were going to-day and as de Greeff had told us that we were on a 48 hours notice basis, many of our people decided to hitch hike to Hanover and Hamburg for the day.

Half way through the morning Russell invited me to come out on his raft with him - went on it and spent a thoroughly enjoyable morning punting round the lake. We saw several shoals of small fish.

We had a quick lunch and then went out on the raft again. Russell noticed that one of the barrels was coming loose and so we put into port for repairs, which Russell had completed in about half an hour.

We were just putting out to sea again, when George Woodwark dashed up to the bank and said that a Dispatch rider had just come from Celle to say that the Aircraft were waiting at Celle and due to leave at 3 o'clock - the time was now ten to three! Tom Crisp answered the message and managed to postpone their leaving until 6 o'clock. We were then told that transport would be leaving from outside the mess at 3.30.

Went up to the tent to find George hastily packing the remainder of his kit - fortunately except for my blankets I was already packed up. Packed up 3 of my big wine glasses and my panzer coat in my blankets, and was ready.

During the packing we plied two Tommies who were guarding the tents with whisky, gin and any loot which we decided that we could not get home - they were very grateful and were half tight by the time we left.

We then got into our equipment and waited for the transport. Talked to a Lieut - Colonel who told us grisly stories about the Customs, which made our hair stand on end, as we were all packed up to the necks with "liberated stuff".

Then the lorries came and we all piled onto them being extremely careful of our kit. We moved off amid the envious stares of several Tommies, but we had to wait half an hour, while one of the lorries picked up some of the people from the German Hospital.

Then at about 4.30 p.m. we left the Panzertruppen Schule for ever! On the way down we sang hard all the way reserving "Tipperary" until we were actually passing through Celle and if looks could have killed we would have all dropped dead, there and then.

The lorries missed the way to the Airstrip twice and on the second attempt we saw a marvellous piece of bombing by the R.A.F. on a factory - completely wrecked with very few of the surrounding houses damaged.

On the Airstrip we found that the Dakotas were all lined up waiting for us and had been lined up since 3 o'clock. Secretly we were all very glad remembering those three days of waiting when we were coming over.

There was no waiting on the Airport to-day, as they were only too keen to get us off. We bundled into the planes, waited 5 minutes while they warmed up the engines and taxied onto the runway. The engines roared, the pitch rising higher and higher and higher, until you felt sure that something would go bust, then slowly we began to move forwards. Got faster and faster - bumped once or twice then all the bumping stopped and we were Airborne!!

We circled Celle and then set course for home, feeling rather sorry
for the chaps who were still in Hanover and Hamburg as they probably won't
be leaving for 2-3 days as another movement control order has to go through
for them.

We passed over Hanover and noted all the damage which had been done to
the marshalling yards and surrounding districts.   There was nothing else
to see after that, except the Autobahns pointing like long white fingers
to the heart of Germany.

We ran into several thunder storms - one of these just as we were
crossing the Rhine and then the next town we knew we were over was Antwerp,
away down there on our right.   We then flew parallel with the coast.

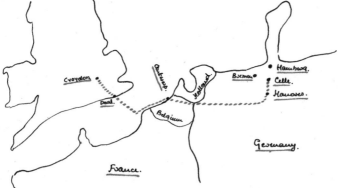

When we reached the French Coast opposite Dover we crossed the channel
and crossed the English coast at Deal and then landed at Croydon at twenty
to ten, with our ears buzzing.

Now came the ordeal which we had all been dreading - the Customs.   We
went in and were given all sorts of forms to fill up - had to hand in our
Allied Military permits and heard over the loud speakers that we were to
hand in our uniforms to-morrow at 2.30.   We then went into another room and
there were our kit bags all laid out on tables.   We were asked to find them

and then asked if we had any "wines spirits or cigarettes" to declare.
I said that I had half a bottle of whisky and the Customs Officer just said
"Oh! really", marked my kit bag and passed on.

We were then asked if we had any letters for anyone in this country.
I said no and then we were let out and clambered onto B.L.A. Lorries which
were going to take us up to London.

On the way up to London we whistled and waved at everybody we passed,
barring a few girls the only people who waved back were policemen, - every
policeman we passed waved to us.

We arrived at Victoria Station at about 10.45, and I started to walk
home, thinking how much happier everyone in Germany looked compared to the
people in England. And yet we had won the War!

Arrived home to an enthusiastic welcome.

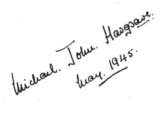

Glossary

?: Question marks are used throughout the diary as shorthand for 'possible' or to indicate an uncertain statistic.

21st Army Group: British-commanded military formation consisting primarily of the British 2nd Army and the First Canadian Army.

Ack-Ack: Nickname for anti-aircraft artillery.

American Typhus Commission: United States of America Typhus Commission, established on 8 December 1942 with the goal of finding the most efficient way of preventing the spread of typhus, primarily for the protection of the US armed forces.

Auschwitz: Name given to a network of camps in and around the town of Oświęcim in Poland, and consisting of three main camps: Auschwitz I (the base or administration camp), Auschwitz II-Birkenau (the extermination camp) and Auschwitz III-Monowitz (the labour camp).

B.L.A.: British Liberation Army, the original name given to the Army of Occupation in Germany following the end of the war.

Barts: St Bartholomew's Hospital.

Battery: An artillery unit generally consisting of between 100 and 200 men and between six and eight guns.

Bengal Famine: The Bengal famine of 1943–1944.

Blakehill Farm: Refers to RAF Blakehill Farm, an air base situated near Cricklade, Wiltshire.

Blockleiter: National Socialist (Nazi) party term given to those prisoners who spoke for huts/blocks.

Bob: A shilling.

Bren carrier: A light armoured vehicle produced to fulfil a number of roles in the British Army, including reconnaissance, transport of large infantry weapons and hauling artillery. All vehicles were armed with the Bren light machine gun.

Brigadier Glyn-Hughes: Brigadier Hugh Llewellyn Glyn-Hughes RAMC, Deputy Director Medical Services, British 2nd Army; was the senior medical officer during the advance across the Rhine. While attached to the 11th Armoured Division he became the first Allied medical officer to enter Belsen.

Bully Beef: Finely minced corned beef in gelatine traditionally packaged in small, oblong-shaped tins.

c.c.s.: Casualty Cleaning Service.

c/o: Country of Origin.

Celle: Capital of Celle District in Lower Saxony, north-eastern Germany.

Colonel Bird: Colonel H.W. Bird, Commander 102 Control Section and Allied Commandant of Belsen.

Colonel Johnstone: Lt Colonel James Alexander Johnstone RAMC, Officer Commanding 32 Casualty Clearing Station; was the senior medical officer at Belsen after its liberation. Belsen was liberated by the British 11th Armoured Division on 15 April 1945, and Johnstone and his unit arrived on 17 April.

Crossing of the Rhine, 1945: Coordinated airborne and amphibious operations named Operation Varsity and Operation Plunder had begun on 24 March and had secured the beach head on the east bank of the River Rhine by 27 March.

Croydon: Location of the Croydon Aerodrome, London's main international airport between 1920 and 1952.

Curzon Line: The Curzon Line was a demarcation line proposed at the end of the First World War between the new Polish republic and Soviet Russia. After the

Yalta Conference in 1945, the line was confirmed, with minor variations, as the new post-war border between Poland and the Soviet Union, which saw large parts of pre-war eastern Poland become part of the Soviet Union.

Dakotas: Name given to the RAF versions of the US Douglas C-47 Skytrain transport aircraft.

Down Aphny: Refers to Down Ampney, the RAF air base located to the northeast of Cricklade, Wiltshire.

Dr Meiklejohn: Dr Arnold P. Meiklejohn of the United Nations Relief and Rehabilitation Administration.

Drugs and dosage: In the diary Michael Hargrave uses opium and aspirin for diarrhoea and pain relief. In the diary he uses various dosage measurements which translates as follows: Aspirin — 15 grains is equivalent to 900 mg (3 aspirin tablets); Opium — ½ grain is equivalent to 30 mg of opium.

Eskimo Nell: *The Ballad of Eskimo Nell*, a traditional bawdy poem.

Flesh and Fantasy: 1943 anthology film starring Edward G. Robinson, Charles Boyer and Barbara Stanwyck; directed by Julien Duvivier; distributed by Universal Pictures.

German doctor: SS-Hauptsturmführer Fritz Klein, a medical officer at the Bergen-Belsen concentration camp from January 1945 until its liberation.

King's Speech: King George VI made a broadcast of thanksgiving to the nation at 21.00 BDST on 8 May 1945.

Kramer: SS-Hauptsturmführer Josef Kramer, commandant of the Bergen-Belsen concentration camp from December 1944 until its liberation.

Laager: Camp.

Light field ambulance: Name given to a mobile medical unit by the British Army.

Limber: A two-wheeled cart designed to support the trailing element of an artillery gun, thus allowing it to be towed.

Lublin Poles: Name given to the pro-Soviet government set up in Poland, which first met in the town of Lublin. This was one of two competing Polish governments, with the other being the anti-Soviet government-in-exile in London.

M.C.: Military Cross, a gallantry decoration then awarded to commissioned officers in the British Army.

Macintosh: A type of waterproof raincoat made from rubberised fabric.

Mae West life jacket: Name given to the first personal flotation device issued to aircrew in the RAF. So-called because of the supposed resemblance the wearing of this jacket gave to the torso of Mae West.

N.A.A.F.I.: Navy, Army and Air Force Institutes, an organisation created by the British government in 1921 to run recreational establishments needed by the British Armed Forces, and to sell goods to servicemen and their families.

PanzertruppenSchule: Refers to the *panzertruppenschule*, the armoured troop training school of the German Army.

Professor Davidson: Professor L.S.P. Davidson, Professor of Medicine at the Polish School of Medicine, University of Edinburgh.

Quartermaster: The unit in charge of distributing supplies and provisions in larger military formations.

R.A.M.C.: Royal Army Medical Corps.

R.C.A.F.: Royal Canadian Air Force.

Ralph: The author's brother.

Russians march into Poland, 1939: The Soviet Union launched an invasion in the east of Poland in September 1939, approximately two weeks after Germany launched its invasion in the west.

S.S.: *Schutzstafel*, paramilitary organisation and military wing of the Nazi party.

Show Business: 1944 musical starring Eddie Cantor, George Murphy, Joan Davis, Nancy Kelly and Constance Moore; directed by Edwin L. Marin; distributed by RKO Radio Pictures.

Shrove Tuesday dinner at Westminster: A tradition started in 1940 by the hospital chaplain at the Westminster Hospital to help raise the spirits of both the doctors and medical students during the Blitz. Sir Stanley Woodwark was guest of honour at the first dinner in 1940.

Sir Stanley Woodwark: Sir Stanley Woodwark CMG CBE MD FRCP, Consulting Physician at the Royal Waterloo Hospital and the Miller General Hospital; President of the Institute of Hygiene; Governor of the Foundling Hospital and the Westminster Hospital.

Tanalbin: Albumin tannate.

Tommies: Plural of 'Tommy Atkins', a colloquial term for a soldier in the British Army.

U.C.H.: University College Hospital.

Ung. Hyd. Ammon.: Ammoniated Mercury, a compound used as an antiseptic ointment for skin conditions.

V-E Day: Victory in Europe Day; the day that the German Instrument of Surrender was signed by General Alfred Jodl at Reims.

W.A.A.F.: Women's Auxiliary Air Force.

(Waffen) S.S.: The armed, military formation of the SS, which paralleled the structure of the German Army and served alongside it, but was never formally part of it, instead remaining the armed wing of the Nazi party.

Wehrmacht: The unified armed forces of Germany between 1935 and 1945, consisting of the army (*Heer*), navy (*Kreigsmarine*) and air force (*Luftwaffe*).